I Learned to Fly

I Learned to Fly
by Pearson Phillips

Frederick Warne

This is a Marix Evans & Chilvers/Thames Head production

First published in Great Britain by Frederick Warne (Publishers) Limited

First published in Great Britain 1982

ISBN 0 7232 2973 2

Printed by GEA Milan
Printed in Italy
Typeset by SP Typesetting

Contents

Introduction

According to the statistics Britain cannot regard itself as an air-minded nation. About one in every ten thousand people has at some time handled the controls of an aeroplane. In America the equivalent figure is nearer one in a thousand. Even Switzerland, covered in mountains, or remote Finland, turn out to be more aviation-minded per head of the population than we are in Britain.

The number of new private pilot licences issued every year by the Civil Aviation Authority has been stuck for some time at roughly the same figure, around 3000 per annum. But it is certainly true that many more people than that think about learning, and may even get some way into their training before giving up trying to fly themselves.

Why do they give up? And why doesn't Britain have more pilots?

A number of reasons are traditionally trotted out the aviation world. The growing expense is one factor, particularly in a time of recession. It does cost money, although not as much as some people think. Around £2500 to secure a Private Pilot's Licence is the figure usually quoted at the time of writing, though it has been rising fast in recent years. Easy finance to make the strain less painful can usually be arranged. Once the licence has been acquired the cost of sharing the ownership of an aircraft or hiring from a club needn't be more than is often spent on a second car or foreign holiday travel. There is also a whole industry dedicated to the proposition that an aeroplane owned by a business can be made into a profitable investment. Pilots don't have to be rich, though it certainly helps.

Another reason often given is that Britain is too small and cluttered with too many airspace restrictions to make flying worth while. It is true that we don't have the broad empty spaces and vast distances enjoyed by private aviators in the United States of America. But there is in fact more freedom to fly in Britain than in some other West European countries. And why should we be restricted to flying in our own island? Private flying brings the rest of Europe within range. Many people, however, find enormous satisfaction in pottering round their home airfields, with occasional cross country marathons into the neighbouring county.

The real reasons seem to be deeper and more subtle than either of these two factors. Private flying in Britain has always traditionally been an activity set apart for a bunch of amateurish enthusiasts. There have, until recently, been few attempts to market the idea of flying training and set up briskly professional organisations and schools.

A number of flying clubs and schools were launched by enthusiasts in the immediate post-war period which never had enough capital or resources to offer an attractive service to would-be students. Costs of training were always kept as low as possible, in the belief that the public would not accept higher charges. As a result, instructors were poorly paid and there were seldom enough aircraft or teachers available to ensure that students who had booked lessons actually found both instructor and aircraft available on time to give them.

As a result vigorous business people (the kind of people who form the backbone of civil flying in other countries) found they could ill afford the time, or the idleness, which seemed to be needed to acquire a licence in Britain. For various reasons the British light aircraft manufacturing industry also failed to survive. Britain's private fliers seemed set to become a small, stand-offish elite living in their own private world and too often without much of a welcome for any beginners wanting to join their group.

There have for some time been signs that all this is finally changing. One factor has been a new enthusiasm for taking to the air, in hang-gliders, balloons and micro-light aircraft if not in conventional light aircraft.

Apart from that some organisations have been projecting flying training on a commercial basis. The London School of Flying at Elstree, one of a group which runs three schools at airfields around London, was chosen as an example of this trend for the course of instruction described in this book. The hourly rates are higher than can be found elsewhere. But the facilities and the thoroughness of instruction also sets out to be of higher quality. Thanks to a system whereby school aircraft are leased from private owners, there are plenty of aircraft available, which helps to cut out delays and forced cancellations.

This school, and others like it, have worked at opening up the world of flying to more people. An essential part of that process is to take some of the mystery out of the whole business of aviation.

Written from the stand-point of one who was learning, rather than as wisdom handed down by an expert, this book is both an attempt to help de-mystify the process of learning to fly and stimulate people to try it. It doesn't aim to teach. But it should make learning easier.

Chapter 1:
How to learn to fly

The first problem for most beginner pilots is to find a flying school which is either near home or near to work. Lists of clubs and schools can be had from several sources. In Britain, the Aircraft Owners and Pilots Association prepares an up-to-date list of 'Where To Fly' each Spring, giving the kind of courses offered, the types of aircraft used, the costs and other useful details. AOPA's address is 50A, Cambridge Street, London SW1V 4QQ (telephone 01-834 5631).

Flying schools range from large establishments like minor colleges full of teachers in uniform blazers to enterprises consisting of one man with a corrugated iron hangar in the corner of a flying field. Appearances are not the sole guide to the quality of the instruction. The CFI (Chief Flying Instructor) tends to imprint his character on a place. It helps if he is the sort of person who is in sympathy with his students, so it is worth seeking him out for a chat. Things to look out for are evidence of a properly worked out programme of slots for lessons, facilities for the all important pre-flight briefings, and enough full time staff to ensure that you will get some continuity of instruction. A school which depends heavily on part time instructors should be regarded with some suspicion, although here again, some are very good – so do investigate first.

Apart from Britain there is the Texas option, a course organised by a British company which flies students from Gatwick to Dallas, puts them up in a hotel for three weeks and gives them sufficient flying instruction to qualify for a licence if they are lucky. The cost of all this works out at less than the rate for doing the same thing in Britain.

The drawback is that it is a fearsomely concentrated experience. And the weather in Dallas, contrary to general belief, is not always kind. Apart from this I have the feeling that if you are going to do your flying in Britain, under British conditions, it is just as well to learn here. Although the Dallas trip could make a stimulating holiday.

Apart from all this, there is the choice of aircraft offered by different schools. The ideal trainer, according to one expert, should be robust, roomy, safe, cheap and possessed of excellent all-round visibility. People argue for several hours on end about which aircraft most nearly approximates to this ideal. One basic difference is the choice between high wing or low wing monoplanes. The Cessna 150/152 is the most common high-wing machine, beloved by some for its sturdy reliability, and despised by others for its cramped quarters and poor visibility over the nose. Having trained on the Gulfstream American AA5A Cheetah, I am probably biassed in its favour. Some people call it 'a tricky aeroplane'. It is not passed for spinning, unlike the Cessna. I found its main delights were the forward visibility and roomy cockpit.

Schools are either 'Approved' or 'Non-Approved' by the Civil Aviation Authority. The difference is not as profound as it might seem, some 'Non-Approved' schools offering a perfectly adequate service, although they may not have all the facilities insisted upon by the CAA inspectors. The main difference is to the students. Learning at a 'Non-Approved' school involves a minimum of forty-three hours flying before a licence can be applied for. At an 'Approved' school the time is thirty-eight hours.

What is involved? A medical examination is the first step. There are certain approved doctors licenced to carry this out, though I personally present myself to the Civil Aviation Authority's own medical department off Kingsway, London. Under 40 you need a test every two years. But over 40 it is an annual test, which cost me £35 when I took it. It is not rigorous, though they do look for heart problems with an ECG test. Eyesight is not a major hurdle, provided you have adequate glasses. (The rules say you must carry a spare pair in the cockpit when flying).

The actual flying can either be spread out over a period of months (though if you take longer than six months you are obliged to do forty-three hours, rather than thirty-eight, even at an 'Approved School'), or concentrated. I was always advised that the more

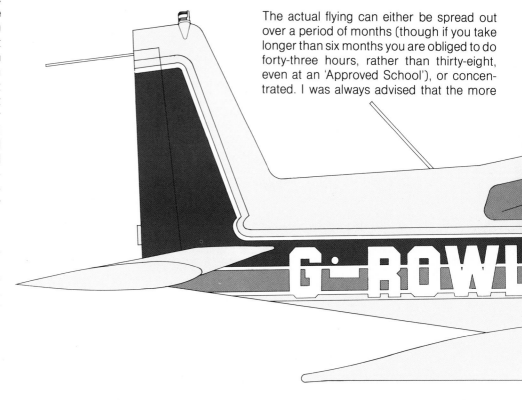

concentrated you make it the better, and I believe that is true. The best technique seems to be to plan out a series of slots for two or three weeks ahead, and make sure that these times are inviolable commitments around which the rest of your business and social life must revolve. One of the most unpopular things which a student can do is cancel his slot at the last moment on a fine day, when there may well have been several other frustrated people who would have jumped at the chance of taking his time. Cancel well in advance if you must. But I found it better to have a short sharp period when the flying was supreme. It got me into a few awkward incidents with my employers, but by this method I managed to get the whole thing over soon enough not to cause too much distress. Apart from the flying there are also the written tests, which are detailed in Chapter nineteen.

People are sometimes surprised to find that they are put into the care of instructors who by no stretch of the imagination could be called hoary old veterans. The fact is that instructing is a method by which would-be professional aviators can build up the hours and the experience necessary before they can qualify for their commercial licences. They can be paid for doing what they want to do, with time for their own study as well.

I was given into the care of Jeanne McCabe, a girl of a ripe twenty-four. Asked by her father at the age of six what she wanted to be when she grew up she had replied with the time-honoured solution: 'Air Hostess'. 'Wouldn't you prefer to be up front flying the things?' said her clever papa. She hadn't actually considered that. But on reflection decided that she would. She was given her first few lessons as a fifteenth birthday present. She solo'd on her seventeenth birthday. A couple of thousand hours later she was a senior instructor at Elstree, working on her commercial licence. Apart from her abilities as a teacher, she demonstrated a sense of humour and a liking for chocolates.

I preceded my actual course with some preliminary reading. One of the longest-standing text books on the art is the series of volumes published by Pitman Publishing under the heading *Flight Briefing For Pilots*, by N H Birch and A E Bramson (who also kindly agreed to keep an eye on this project). Apart from that, Alan Bramson has written a volume called *Be A Better Pilot,* published by Martin Dunitz. I liked this for its examination

of the psychology of safe flying. For those who can take a bit more detail and theory there is the *Flying Training Manual* published by the Aircraft Owners' and Pilots' Association (compiled by AOPA's chairman Ron Campbell). I found it a solid £8 read.

Reading is also, incidentally, a good way of easing into the 'ambience' of flying. I enjoyed *Pilot* magazine, found on major bookstalls. Occasionally I would lash out on a copy of the American monthly *Flying*, which gives a glimpse of a heady, high-powered world of American private flying but also imparts some of the heart-warming folksiness which is part of the tradition of American aviation.

As the day appointed for my first session arrived I found myself faced with a curious problem: what does one wear to learn to fly nowadays? In an early flying training book I found a reference to a special tailored leather helmet made up at a London outfitters. That didn't seem quite the thing. So I rang for some advice. 'You can control the inside of a modern aeroplane to whatever climate you like', I was told. 'But wear a light, cotton shirt, because you will probably find yourself sweating a bit at first. And rubber soled shoes, if possible. The only thing you have to watch is not catching a cold walking out to the aircraft'. I found this very helpful.

Someone gave me a pair of chamois leather aviator's gloves (to absorb moisture from heated palms) and American cap with a long peak bearing some Air Marshal-like gold 'scrambled egg'. I haven't had the courage to wear those yet. But I will soon.

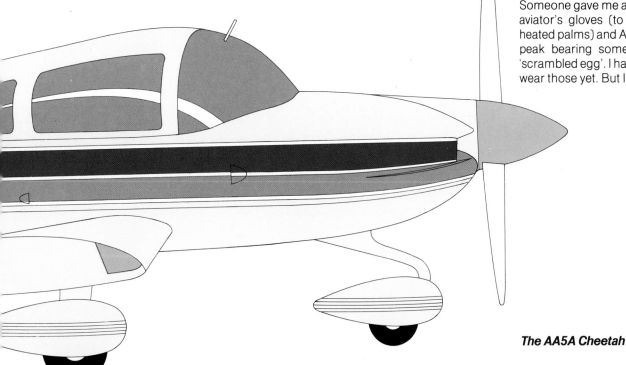

The AA5A Cheetah

Chapter 2:
What do you do first: check, check and check again

An early step for most would-be aviators is the so-called Trial Lesson. It isn't really a lesson. It is more of a ritual meeting between student, instructor and aeroplane in order to see how they will all get on with each other. There is a chat on the ground followed by a short flight, during which the instructor will attempt to make the whole business seem as attractive as possible. It is quite likely that the flight will include a seductive spell in the clean, smooth sunlit world above the clouds. You should make the most of it if it does. Hours of grind nearer the ground will have to be endured before you are allowed up in that enchanted world again.

Jeanne estimated that only about one person in seven or eight who took a trial lesson at Elstree went on to do a course. Some people look on it as a one-off experience, a joy-ride, a taste of the unknown. Trial lessons are also given away as birthday presents to people with no intention of gaining a licence. Others discover that the whole business of sitting in a comparatively cramped and noisy bit of machinery bumping and lurching about

the sky is not what they thought flying was about. People who wish to make a favourable impression on their instructors from the start (don't we all?) should ask questions: What does this do? What does that do?

'It's the ones who just hang on tensely, not saying a word, that I know I am going to have problems with,' said Jeanne. Whereupon I naturally relaxed and talked all the time. In most trial lessons the instructor does let the student take over the control column. It would be an exaggeration to say that this feels anything like flying it, however. In my own case, as with most people, I felt that the aircraft was still the master and that I had as much influence on it as a child having its first seaside donkey ride. Nor is this an impression that remains for only the Trial Lesson. I didn't really begin to feel confident of controlling the aircraft, bringing it to heel, until some time after I'd flown solo. Even then there were always likely to be surprises. The skill of piloting, I discovered, lies in eliminating all possible surprises and knowing how to react when, inevitably, they do occur.

Pre-starting Checks

In my own case I was plunged straight away into the business of eliminating surprises by being handed a shiny, spiral-bound ten-page booklet entitled: *AA5A Cheetah Check List*. The one I used had been prepared, and copyrighted, by the London School of Flying. But every aircraft type has one and it is a basic tool of the trade.

There are three main types of checks set out in this booklet. Most are commonsense, as we shall see.

1 Checks done on the ground to make sure there is nothing wrong with the aircraft before we even get around to starting up.

2 Checks done in the aircraft to make sure that she is not likely to let us down either

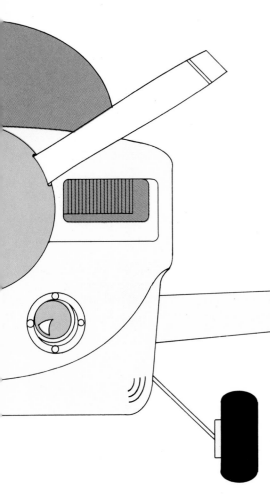

before take-off, during the flight or on landing. Included in this group are also a set of procedures for switching off and making the aircraft safe after the flight and leaving it for others (as the landladies put it) in the condition we would wish to find it.

3 Emergency checks, printed in red, for action to be taken on the occurrence of such things as engine failure or fires. These ones are supposed to be committed to memory, a point indicated in the check list by a solid line down the left hand margin opposite each check (some of the other checks get this treatment as well). As a point of guidance, I was told that the checks to be memorised are those that occur when there is a shortage of time for laboriously running a finger along the printed page

and when some attention needs to be reserved for what is happening in the world outside. But having gone through a set of memorised checks, it does no harm, if a spare moment occurs, to run through the list to see if any of them have been left out.

In my own case a full Trial Lesson was thought to be a waste of time and money, as I was obviously set on going through with the process of learning, come what may. So I was led through all the details of taking over an aeroplane and checking it through from the first day, part of an exercise the schools call 'Aircraft Familiarisation'. What follows now should enable a pilot to take over any aeroplane anywhere and set off with some degree of confidence that it is not going to let him down.

In a highly organised and well maintained flying school we are unlikely to be given a dud aeroplane. But there may be a time when we wish to borrow some unknown mud-spattered monster which has been lying exposed to raw nature for days in a

backwoods flying field. In such a case the check list comes into its own.

The extent of the checks depend upon whether the machine is flying for the first time in the day, or is merely between flights (when it gets the more cursory so-called 'Transit Check').

'Don't just mouth the checks', I was told. 'Accompany each one with some kind of action, if it only involves pointing at the thing you are checking'. It is important to avoid drifting into a meaningless litany. Even the best run establishments might just possibly harbour someone who has done a heavy, destructive landing and has been too embarrassed to report the resulting damage. During my training an aircraft on the field was found to have had its fuel tanks doctored with sugar by some unknown malefactor with an apparent grudge against aviation. Careful pre-flight checking discovered it before any serious harm was done.

And so, to the checks.

Pre-starting Checks
(For the first flight of the day)

Cockpit Preparations

1 Aircraft Documents . . . Check
I quickly realised that there is a lot of paper-work involved with flying, quite apart from the writing of cheques. The School itself has a large form called a Flight Authorisation Sheet, on which are entered the details of the aircraft, the people on board, date, type of training to be covered, and area of the flight. The instructors fill them out before each flight, although when solo time arrives some of the signing has to be done by the student.

The aircraft documents proper were kept in special files and were available for inspection when asked for. It is a good idea to have a look at them occasionally, even when flying bureaucratically immaculate school aircraft, so that we know what to look for. Most imposing among them is the Certificate of Airworthiness, which has the dates of its validity on the back. There is also a Mainten-ance Document, a type of aerial Test Certifi-cate, which shows when the required Civil Aviation Authority maintenance checks were carried out and when the next ones are due. (Required checks by a certified engineer are quite frequent).

The L.S.F., like most schools, also had what is called a 'Tech. Log' for each aircraft. This not only records how much longer there is to go before the next general 75-hour check is due, but also has a space in which pilots can list any minor faults, like spongey brakes or a failed landing light. Looking at this list told us what to expect in the way of minor irri-tations. The school's maintenance staff keep an eye on these tech. logs, of course.

There was, therefore, a fair bit of paper to look at before we got anywhere near the aircraft itself.

2 Magneto Switch . . . Off
It is essential to be sure that the engine is not live while the checks are being done. The ignition is switched on with a key. The only way the key can be taken out is when the ignition is switched off, so as long as the keys are out the magnetos are off. The normal practice is to lay the keys on top of the fascia panel, handy for when we come to start her up. BUT WE KEEP THEM OUT WHILE DOING THE CHECKS.

3 Control Locks . . . Stowed
The control column is normally locked by a pinning device to stop the controls being blown about by the wind and damaged when the aeroplane is on the ground. The pin has a large red metal flag on it, which is normally arranged so that it lies in front of the engine switches, thus discouraging any absent-minded person from trying to start up and move off before taking the control lock out. We take it out and put it in the right hand side 'glove pocket'.

4 Loose Articles/Baggage etc . . . Stowed
I found it quite acceptable to lay briefcases, jackets and other odds and ends on the back seat of the Cheetah, although for Spinning or Stalling it is necessary to put them some-where more secure, where they won't fly about the cabin. There is a handy little pocket down by the left leg which takes maps, flight plans and bits of paper which will be needed on the voyage.

5 Parking Brake . . . On
It should have been left on by the last pilot. The knob is marked 'Pull On', so if it is out the brakes are on.

6 Fire Extinguisher . . . Check
Normally under the pilot's (or left hand) seat. If it isn't, look under the right hand (or instructor's) seat. (The seat cushions lift up easily). It also makes sense to discover how to work it.

7 First Aid Kit . . . Check
It's in a pocket on the back of the front seats.

8 Radio and Nav Equipment . . . Off
We make sure that all the various radio knobs are turned to off. They are not needed at this stage and will help to run the battery down if they are on.

9 Battery Master Switch . . . On
One of a pair of switches to the right of the magneto switch. Putting it on turns on the battery power, so that we can now test some of the things running off the battery. However, unless there is an independent outside elec-tric supply, don't take too long . . .

10 Fuel Contents . . . Check
There are two gauges, for left and right tanks.

11 Flashing Beacon/Strobes . . . Check
Each switch in the line of electrical switches is conveniently marked. We just press a switch and look out to see if the appropriate light works.

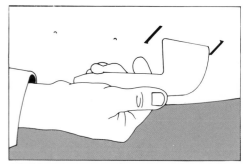

12 Pitot Heater . . . Check
Another of the line of electrical switches. Testing this one involves getting across to the pitot tube, under the end of the port wing, and feeling it to see if it is warming up when switched on. The impact of the air flowing into this tube is what makes the airspeed indicator function. If there is a possibility of ice forming on the aircraft it is important to have some heat available to prevent this tube becoming blocked. At least we shall con-tinue to know our airspeed, a vital piece of information, as we shall discover.

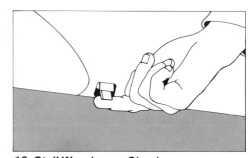

13 Stall Warning . . . Check
This is a small flap on the leading edge of the right wing which cleverly lifts up and makes a warning buzz in the cockpit when the air-craft is flying nose high with the airflow coming from below, the symptoms of an imminent stall and loss of flying speed. We shall know all about this when we come to 'Stalling', Chapter eleven. For the moment it will be enough to lift the flap by hand to see if the appropriate buzz comes from the cockpit.

14* Landing Light . . . Check

The last switch on the row and we need to nip round to the front of the aircraft to see if it has come on. This check and the next one are marked with an asterisk (*) to show that they may be missed out if 'no part of the planned flight takes place at night'. Maybe so. But a landing light is a useful thing to have round a crowded airfield even in daylight. It helps to let everybody else know where you are.

15* Nav and Cockpit Lights . . . Check

The remaining switches. And if you need to test them the navigation lights are at each wing tip and the rear end of the fuselage.

16 Battery Master Switch . . . Off

Having tested the battery-run electrics, we get rid of the power for the moment.

These 'Cockpit Preparations' can be done without actually sitting in the cockpit. The switches and gauges can be reached from the black treading surface alongside the cockpit, which will avoid the bother of clambering in and out to do all the exterior things like feeling the pitot tube and working the stall warning tab.

Pre-starting checks   7   3   2 9 16   15 11   6 10 5   8   12 14

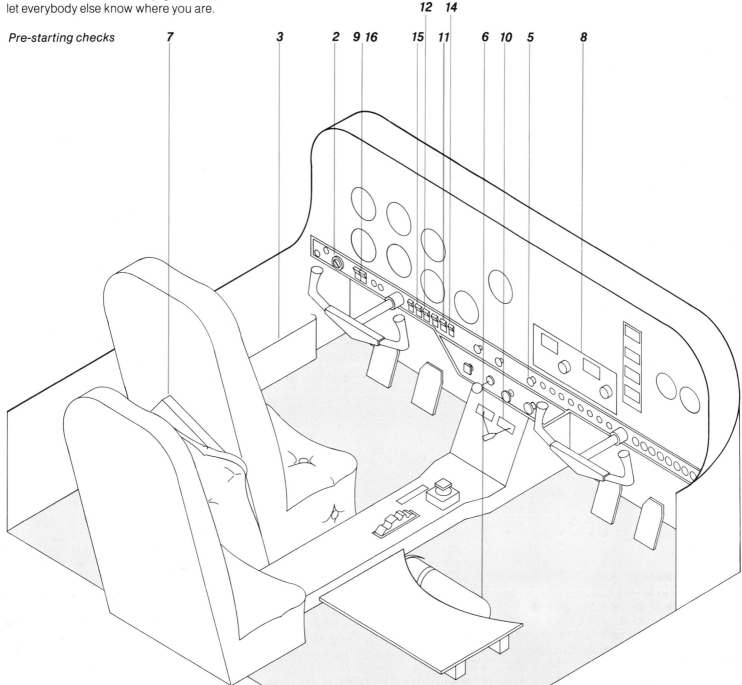

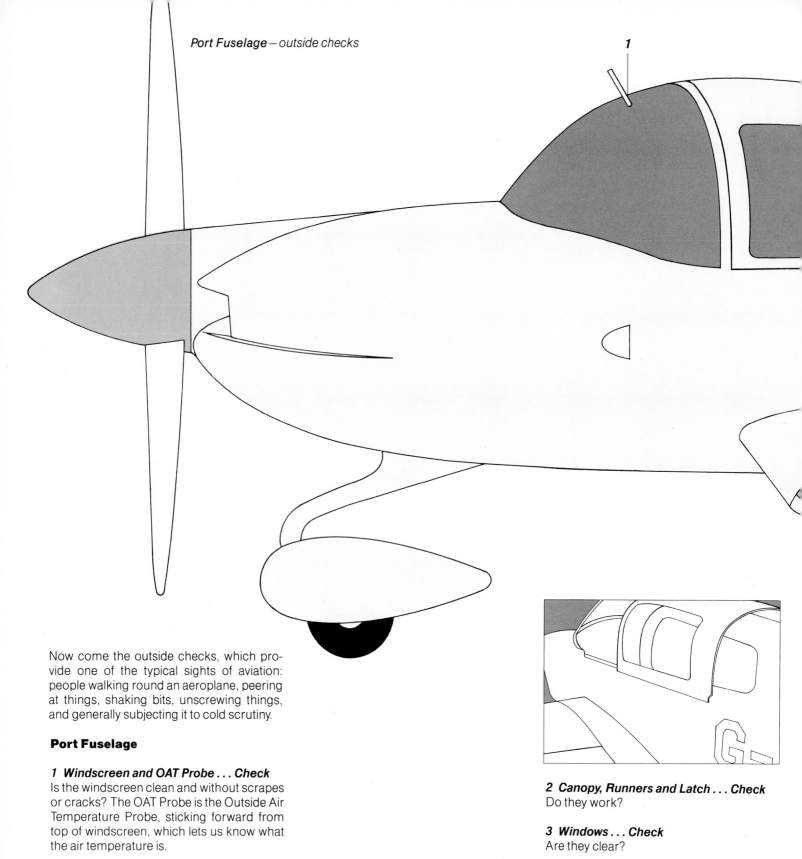

1

Now come the outside checks, which provide one of the typical sights of aviation: people walking round an aeroplane, peering at things, shaking bits, unscrewing things, and generally subjecting it to cold scrutiny.

Port Fuselage

1 Windscreen and OAT Probe ... Check

Is the windscreen clean and without scrapes or cracks? The OAT Probe is the Outside Air Temperature Probe, sticking forward from top of windscreen, which lets us know what the air temperature is.

2 Canopy, Runners and Latch ... Check
Do they work?

3 Windows ... Check
Are they clear?

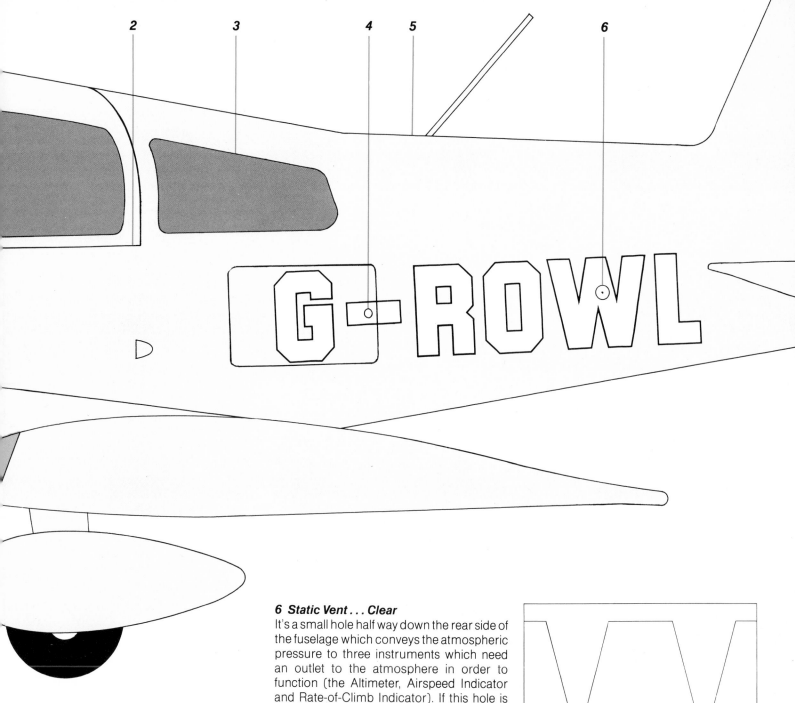

4 Baggage Door . . . Secure

We just have to make sure it is locked and isn't going to fly open in flight.

5 Skin . . . Check

Just pat it lightly to see that there are no rattles and that it is still fastened securely to the inner structure.

6 Static Vent . . . Clear

It's a small hole half way down the rear side of the fuselage which conveys the atmospheric pressure to three instruments which need an outlet to the atmosphere in order to function (the Altimeter, Airspeed Indicator and Rate-of-Climb Indicator). If this hole is blocked we shall get a misleading message from them. What could block it? Ice and snow is the obvious culprit. But I was told with a seemingly straight face that insects sometimes nest in it! Presumably it is then necessary to call for the de-infestation officer. It is not a good idea to blow into it. Sensitive instruments do not take kindly to such treatment.

Tail Section

1 Fin Surface and Aerials . . . Check
Is the fin firm? Are there any broken or loose aerials?

2 Tailplane Surface . . . Check
I notice most people grab it and shake it up and down a bit to see if it is still bolted on. Not too hard!

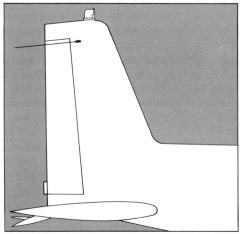

3 Elevator and Anti-Servo Tab . . . Check
The elevators can be moved up and down to see that all their joints, pulleys and swivels are working. At the same time we can see that the anti-servo tab, or trim tab (the small flaps at the back of the elevators which are a device operated from the cockpit to trim the aircraft) are moving in harmony with the elevators.

4 Rudder/Nav Light and Anti-Collision Light . . . Check
We can give the rudder a tweak to see that it is firm and working. At this point I was advised to have a look underneath the rear of the fuselage. It has been known for people to do a tail-heavy landing which scrapes the rear of the fuselage along the ground. Signs of damage from that need looking out for. Also, stones can occasionally get kicked up and jammed into the rudder and elevator mechanism.

5 Elevators and Anti-Servo Tab . . . Check

6 Tailplane Surface . . . Check

7 Fin Surface and Aerials . . . Check
All the same as above, on the other side.

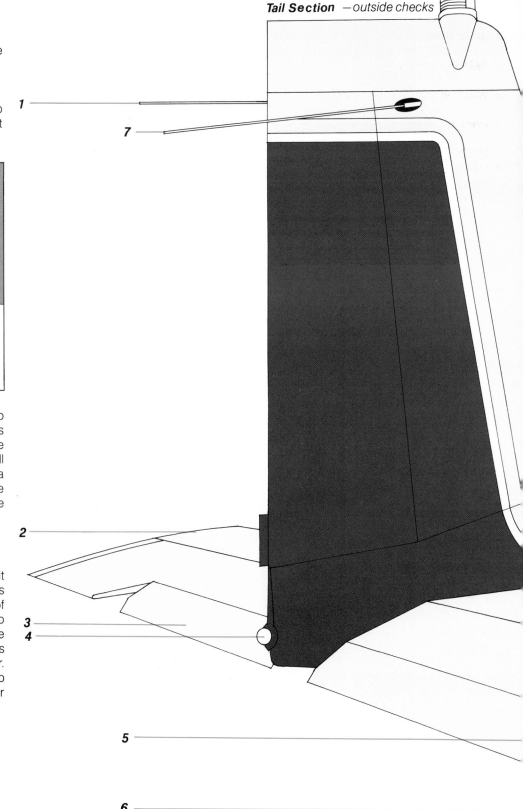

Starboard Fuselage

1 Static Vent ... Clear

2 Skin ... Check

3 Windows and Canopy ... Check

4 Upper Surface and Aerials ... Check

5 Under Surface and Aerials ... Check
A repeat of the Port Side checks, with a bit more attention to the top and bottom of the fuselage.

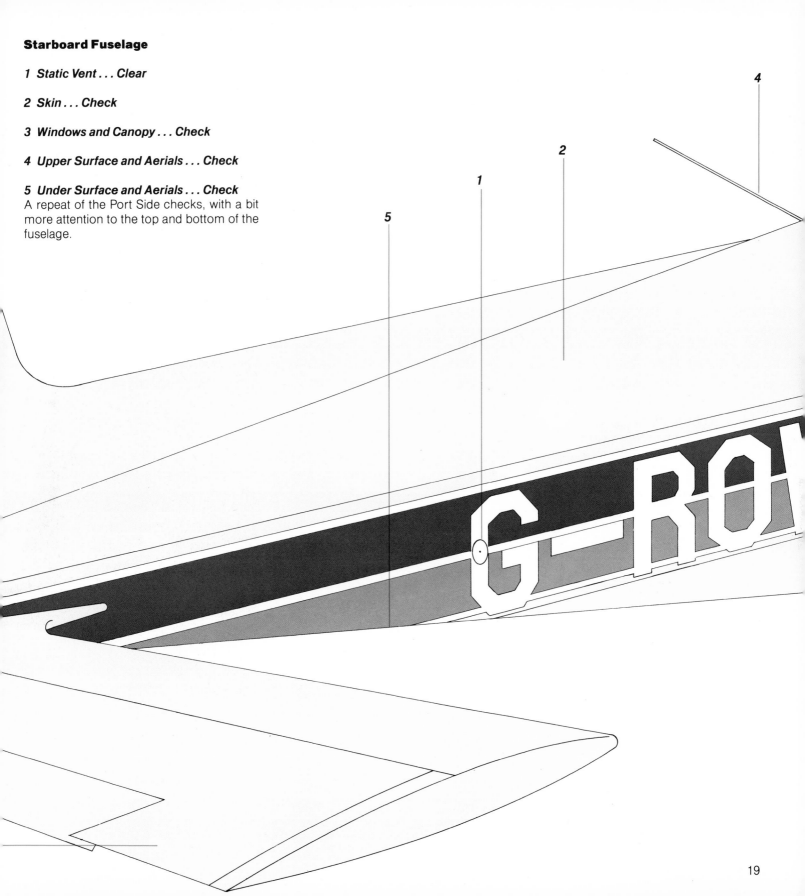

Starboard Wing

1 Flap ... Check

At this stage there is little more to do than see that they haven't been damaged and are firmly attached. They are electrically operated from the cockpit and we shall be testing that they work later, when the engine is generating some electrical power.

2 Aileron and Trim Tab ... Check

We can move the aileron up and down, having first made sure that there isn't a ladder, petrol drum or other obstruction sitting under the aileron on the other wing. These are sensitive, fragile bits of apparatus. Moving one aileron up will automatically shove the other one down, and it would not do to clonk it against some solid object. (It is worth checking that one *does* go up as the other one goes down. It has been known for them to be incorrectly rigged). The trim tab on the Cheetah is a solid bit of sheet metal stuck at a permanent angle on the aileron for balancing purposes.

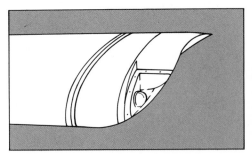

3 Wing Tip and Lights ... Check

We are looking for signs of someone having crunched a wing tip while taxying along the ground. The clear plastic covers on the wing tip navigation lights are usefully squidgy, so that they spring back into place if you do have a mild encounter with something.

4 Upper and Lower Surfaces ... Check

Again we are looking for other people's mistakes. Underneath the wing tip is a tell-tale spot. If an awkward landing has been made on one wheel with one wing down this is the bit that will get scraped.

5 Fuel Tank, Vent and Drain ... Check

We have seen what the fuel gauges say in No. 10 of the Cockpit Checks, but they cannot be trusted to tell the truth on every occasion. The filler cap on top of the wing can be opened by lifting the flap and turning. (It's good practice to put it back so that the flap is facing the rear and there is no chance of the wind helping to lift it up). The printed message 'Grade 100 or 100 LL Min' refers to the grade and octane rating of the fuel needed, 'LL' standing for Low Lead. Each tank holds approximately 26 U.S. gallons (well, it's an American aeroplane). By opening the cap and peering in it is possible to estimate roughly how much is on board. There is a bar across the middle of the tank, and when the fuel is just up to the level of that bar there are nineteen gallons in it. Hence the query voiced frequently between instructor and student at Elstree when checking tanks. 'Is it above or below the bar?'

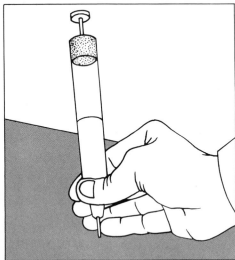

Having checked the quantity we now check for water in the tank. It can get there through condensation on the tank walls if the right moist, cold conditions are present. Being heavier than petrol it sinks, so we can test for water by pressing a tubular fuel drainer into a drain at the bottom of the tank, under the wing. 100 LL Aviation Gasoline (AVGAS) is dyed blue, so the water will show clear in the tube if it is present.

There are two of these drains on each wing, one inboard of the tank in the lowest part of the fuel system. Both need to be dealt with and it is important to check that, having drained, the sprung drain valve goes snugly back into place and doesn't allow fuel to carry on dribbling from the tank, which can happen if we manage to insert a bit of grit into the valve. What we are looking for is a tube of exclusively blue liquid (filling the fuel tester about half full is enough).

6 Stall Warning Trigger ... Check

I have to admit that I never quite understood this. We have already checked that it was working, with the battery switched on. I suppose we are now checking to see if it is still there.

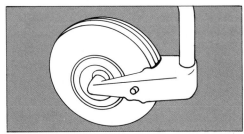

7 Landing Gear ... Check

We are looking at the condition of the tyre, checking that it has plenty of tread all round and isn't badly cracked. There is also usually a paint mark on the tyre sidewall and the corresponding part of the rim. These two paint marks should coincide, within a couple of centimetres. They are there to show up any creep of the tyre round the rim, which can do violence to tube and valve. We can also take a look at the disc brakes on the wheel, and check for any leak of hydraulic fluid by running a finger along the brake pipe. We are also (to state the obvious) looking to see that the tyre is properly blown up and not soft and spongey.

8 Chocks ... Clear

This is the moment to drag the wooden chocks away from the starboard wheel, if any have been put there. They are there as a safety measure to back up the braking system. At Elstree there was a rule that they should be placed on the grass well behind the line of aircraft. It is a good habit to get into, because loose chocks left lying in people's way can catch a wheel during taxying and swing an aircraft round with alarming and possibly expensive results.

Apart from chocks, aircraft can be tied down with ropes fed through small rings on the airframe and anchored to heavy lumps of concrete, especially on windy days. It is very embarrassing to try and move off while still attached to the ground in this way. The fact that the check list doesn't include a section saying 'Tie downs . . . Remove' is one example of the fact that slavish faith in check lists is not enough.

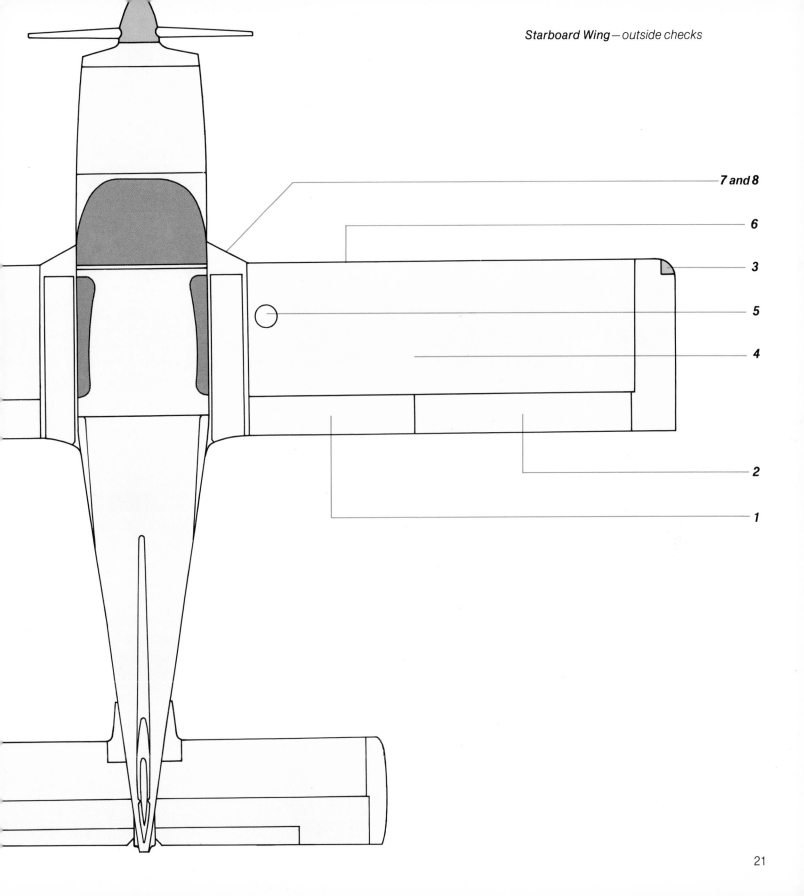

7 and 8

6

3

5

4

2

1

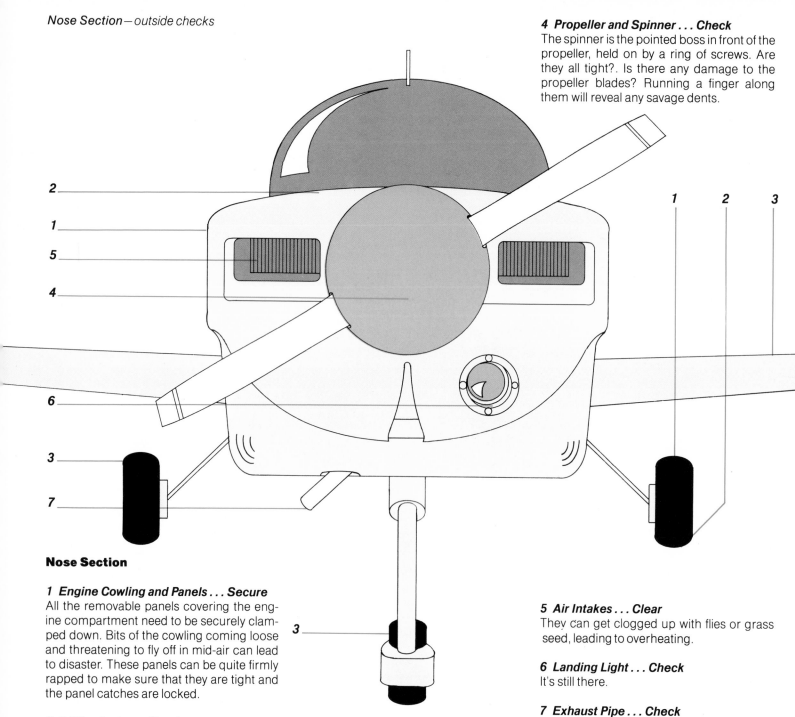

4 Propeller and Spinner . . . Check

The spinner is the pointed boss in front of the propeller, held on by a ring of screws. Are they all tight?. Is there any damage to the propeller blades? Running a finger along them will reveal any savage dents.

Nose Section

1 Engine Cowling and Panels . . . Secure

All the removable panels covering the engine compartment need to be securely clamped down. Bits of the cowling coming loose and threatening to fly off in mid-air can lead to disaster. These panels can be quite firmly rapped to make sure that they are tight and the panel catches are locked.

2 Oil Contents . . . Check

The dip stick is attached to the oil filler cap, which can be reached through a panel on the top right hand nose panel. The figure '8', standing for 8 U.S. quarts, is the maximum level on the dip stick. Anything between that and the '6' mark is permissible. Below that we need to put some more in.

3 Landing Gear . . . Check

Once more we are looking for tyre condition and creep, from the nosewheel. There may also be chocks to be removed.

5 Air Intakes . . . Clear

They can get clogged up with flies or grass seed, leading to overheating.

6 Landing Light . . . Check

It's still there.

7 Exhaust Pipe . . . Check

For the first flight of the day check it won't harm to manhandle it. On other occasions it might well be painfully hot. Nudge it with your foot if you must.

8 Engine Cowling and Panels . . . Secure

The same treatment for Port Side panels as for the Starboard ones.

22

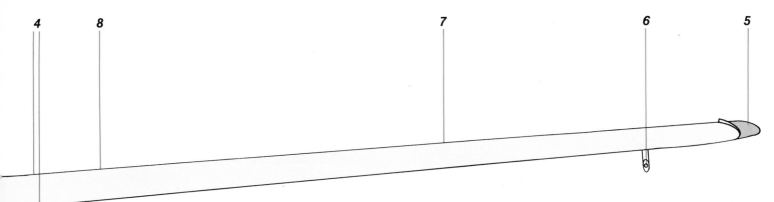

4   8   7   6   5

Port Wing

1 Chocks . . . Clear
We now begin roughly the same treatment around the Port Wing as for the Starboard one, in reverse order.

2 Landing Gear . . . Check

3 Fuel Tank, Vent and Drain . . . Check

4 Upper and Lower Surfaces . . . Check

5 Wing Tip and Lights . . . Check

6 Pitot Head . . . Clear
The hole at the front of the tube needs to be clear of any obstructions that might hinder the passage of air to the airspeed indicator.

7 Aileron and Trim Tab . . . Check

8 Flap . . . Check

Having arrived where we set out from, it is now time to climb in. I was taught that there is even a neat and acceptable way of doing this. The seat cushions fold up. We can therefore lift them and step onto the frame underneath, thus avoiding mud on the seat cover. It is then easy to hold on to the top of the windscreen frame, put our feet into the floor well and ease ourselves down while folding the seat under our bottom at the same time. Learning this neat entry into the Cheetah's fairly awkward cockpit saved me from making too much of an exhibition of myself before I had even started.

These checks may seem tedious. But they become part of the routine of flying, much as grooming a horse becomes a necessary and even enjoyable part of riding one. They are vital for the simple fact that in an aeroplane it is not possible to pull into the side of the road and ring for a mechanic if something seems wrong. We have to get all our problems over before setting off.

For taking on an aeroplane that has already flown that day, the so-called 'Transit Check' (which is also done when stopping somewhere en route to another destination) lets us off more lightly. In the cockpit we just have to check that the brakes are on and the magneto switch is off before turning on the battery to look at what the fuel gauges say. Then it's off with the battery again. Our walk round the aeroplane follows the same course and is a general check that all the controls are working and the airframe is in good conditions. We do look into the fuel tanks to see whether the gauges are telling the truth, and we do check the oil and the landing gear.

As my 'Trial Lesson' was more of a lesson than a trial I was also introduced to the set of checks that are gone through once we have got ourselves settled into the cockpit, which include such vital matters as whether the control column is actually moving the controls (we look outside to see whether it is, an operation that needs some neck craning when it comes to testing the rudder). To my amazement I was even allotted the task of starting the engine on this trial outing (a task which I have gone into fully in Chapter four). As it burst into life I felt a considerable sense of achievement. In these early days a little success goes a long way.

Chapter 3:
How do you work it? The control surfaces

Left aileron

Left flap

Rudder

Trim tab

Left elevator

My first mistake was to assume that learning to fly would start with clambering into an aeroplane. The real lesson began, not in a cockpit, but in a small wood-partitioned cubicle of the kind used to interview customers in an employment exchange. There was a table, two chairs and a blackboard.

The small Briefing Room was to be central to the whole business. I was to spend more time there than in an aeroplane. This is why learning to fly differs from learning most other active pastimes, particularly learning to drive a car. Knowing how to move the plane around the air and handle the controls is only part of being a pilot, and for some people may not even be the hardest part.

Flying is an introduction to a new world, with a new language and a new way of thinking. Caution, self-discipline and careful planning are vital for survival. In addition we need to know what makes our machine behave the way it does in order to know how to treat it kindly and make sure that, in return, it keeps us out of trouble.

It all seems closer to embracing a new religion than learning a skill. Much of it is imbibed in this wooden cell. That is why a notebook and pen are vital to the student pilot. A small tape recorder would also be useful. (Notice that we are 'students' in aviation, rather than 'learners'. In the flying world the belief is that everyone is always learning something new.)

So it was on a warm afternoon in July that Jeanne sat me in front of the blackboard to explain what Lesson One was all about. 'At

this stage I am not going to try to teach you to fly', she said. 'I just want you to get used to the aircraft. We are going to see what happens to the aeroplane when we do certain things to the controls.'

Anyone who has read Biggles probably knows what a joy-stick or control column is

and also roughly what happens when it is pulled hard back or shoved to one side. But the truth is that aeroplanes do a lot more than is mentioned in adventure stories. A movement of the control column often will result in not just one thing happening to the aeroplane, but two things. Something called 'further effect' or 'secondary effect' comes

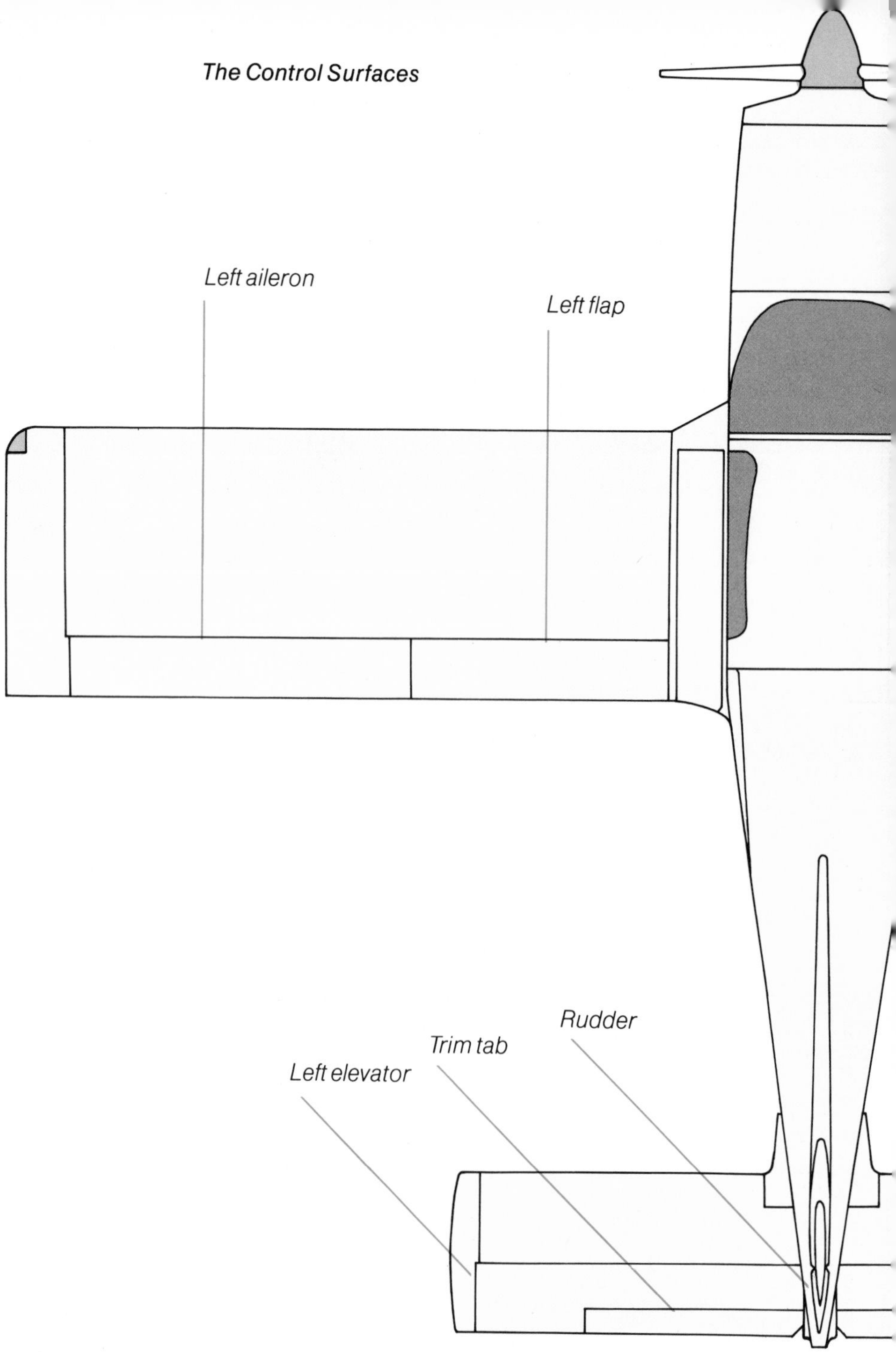

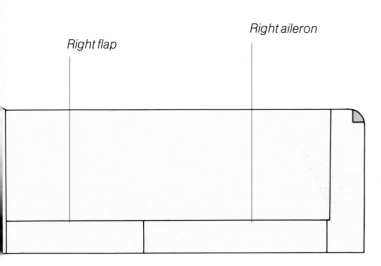

Right flap

Right aileron

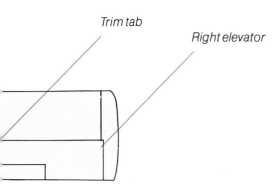

Trim tab

Right elevator

from the instrument panel. This yoke (named presumably after the half collar worn by oxen, carthorses and milkmaids) works like the stick of old, the wheel turning left and right and the whole thing moving backwards and forwards.

Apart from the yoke or control column (as it is generally termed) the main item we have to worry about at this stage are the rudder pedals, one for each foot. The technique with them is to put heels on the floor and move them with the upper part of the foot.

One thing we shall notice when we get in the air. The control column need hardly be moved at all to make the aircraft react. It is very sensitive. As Jeanne said: 'All you have to do is put pressure on it, rather than pull or push it about. As we shall see, the higher your speed the more sensitive it is'. Instructors usually talk about 'putting on back pressure' or 'putting on forward pressure'. It is the kind of gentle reminder a rider will give a well-trained horse. This sensitive treatment won't work if the pilot is gripping the yoke with the whites of his knuckles showing. He won't as they say, be able to 'feel the aeroplane'. Most of the time it can be held between the thumb and two fingers of the left hand, leaving the right hand free to do things which we shall come to later.

The rudder pedals are a different matter. They are heavier, more brutal objects requiring rather more force. This is deliberate. While hands are delicate, capable of making and registering subtle movements, feet are clumsier objects incapable of doing justice to a sensitive control. The rudder control is therefore built to need a deliberate force to make it work.

One thing all the controls need is a smooth, gradual touch. No sudden jerks or yanks. That will strain the aeroplane and its controls and be uncomfortable for the passengers.

into play. To explain what that is Jeanne produced a model made out of scraps of wood and metal. It boasted a movable control column and rudder pedals, connected, as in the real thing, to the elevators, ailerons and rudder (known as the 'control surfaces'). Anyone wanting to master the theory painlessly could get hold of or make a similar

model, which need only be a fairly crude elementary affair.

The model had a simple 'stick' as a control column. But most modern aircraft, including the type I was learning on, have what is called a 'yoke', which looks like half a steering wheel stuck on the end of a tube projecting

So much for how to move the controls. But what happens when we do move them? The model helped reveal all. At this stage it was not a question of going deeply into aerodynamics. What I got was some basic information which many students (including me) will think they know already. (I found that I didn't know all of it, however).

The Elevators

Firstly: the backwards and forwards movement of the control column. This moves the elevators, the control surfaces on the tailplane. A backwards pull raises them. The air striking the raised elevator pushes the tail down and makes the aircraft pivot like a see-saw, bringing the nose up. With sufficient engine power, this makes the aircraft start climbing. Like a car going up hill, it will also fly more slowly. A forward push has exactly the opposite effect, lowering the elevators, pushing the nose down and making the aircraft go faster. Every movement has a name. This one, worked by the elevators, is called 'pitch'.

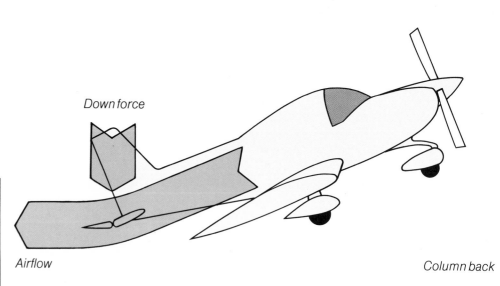

Down force

Airflow

Column back

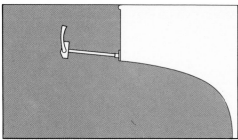

Backward pressure on the control column will put the nose up

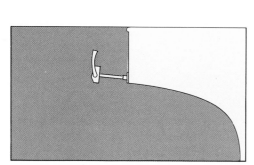

Forward pressure on the control column will put the nose down

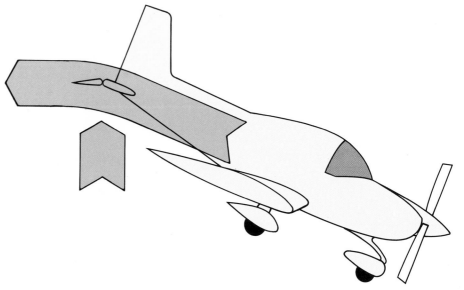

Column forward

The Ailerons

Secondly: the side to side movement of the column (or of the wheel of a yoke). This moves the ailerons, the two control surfaces on the back outer part of each wing. A move to the left puts the right aileron down and the left aileron up, which makes the aircraft roll to the left. Why? What the ailerons do is alter the amount of lift each wing is producing. An aileron going down increases the lift, but an aileron sticking up decreases it. It is obvious that if one wing is generating more lift (or 'flying better') than the other wing, that wing will go up while the other one goes down, tilting the whole machine, or (to use the correct word) rolling it. Whichever way we push the control column or turn the yoke, that wing will go down. This movement is called, sensibly, 'roll'.

But this is not all the ailerons do. There is also one of those 'further effects', or 'secondary effects'. As the aeroplane rolls we shall find it turning as well. The nose will swing round in the direction of the downward wing. The full details of why this happens will be examined later. Suffice it to say at this point that the lift force of wings at an angle does not exactly counter the aircraft's weight and the pull of gravity. So it begins to slip sideways, down towards the lower wing. This means that a side wind will hit the aeroplane, all the way from the nose, down the body (or fuselage) to the big fin and rudder at the rear. In the old days an aviator would have felt a distinct breeze on one side of his face. But the pivot point or centre of gravity of an aircraft is up at the weighty front end, where the engine, pilot and fuel are. This means there is much more of a surface behind the pivot point for a side wind to hit (including the great sail-like fin) than there is in front. The side wind will therefore swing the tail round like a weather cock, pivoting the nose in the other direction. So when we bank we also turn. (We sink as well, of course, unless we do something to stop it. But more of that later).

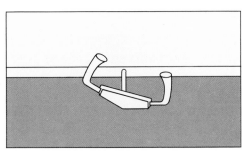

A turn of the control column to the right will raise the left wing

The effects of the ailerons

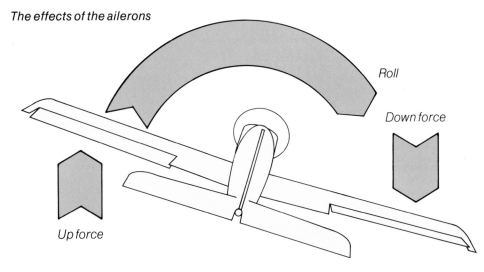

Roll

Down force

Up force

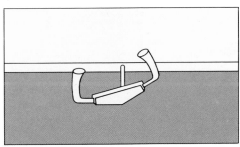

A turn of the control column to the left will drop the left wing

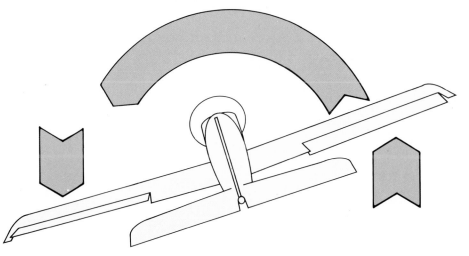

The Rudder

Thirdly: the rudder pedals. Pressing the right rudder pedal moves the rudder surface on the rear of the fin to the right. The air striking it moves the whole tail to the left, thereby pivoting the nose to the right. Thus the right pedal swings the nose round to the right, and vice versa. This movement is called the yaw (which etymologists may care to know, is from the Old Norse *jaga*, to swing). But something that may disconcert Old Norsemen and sailors in general is that using the rudder is not the way to alter course. Air being slippery all that happens when we yaw the nose to the right is that momentum

The effects of the rudder

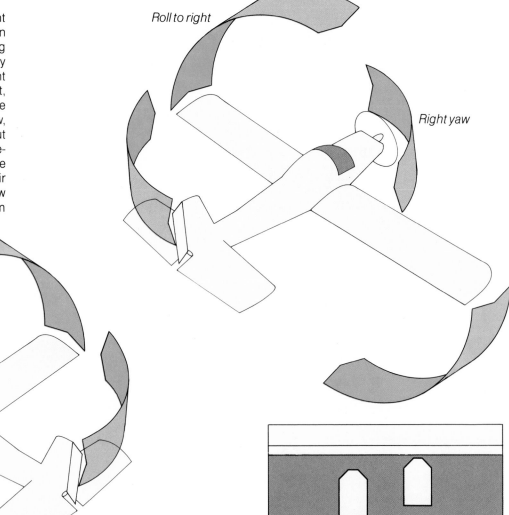

The right rudder pedal will move the nose to the right, and the left wing will rise

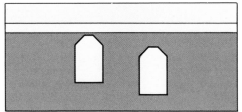

The left rudder pedal will move the nose to the left, and the right wing will rise

moves the aircraft on a sideways skid in much the same way that a car will slide sideways on ice. To turn we have to do something else, as we shall discover.

But this skidding movement is not all the rudder does. There is also an interesting 'further effect'. As can be seen easily with a model, an aeroplane swivelling round to the right will move its left wing further and therefore faster than its right wing. It is like a column of soldiers wheeling in line abreast. The ones on the inside of the turn will almost be marking time, while the outside ones will have to lengthen their stride to keep the

ranks straight. But the faster a wing goes the more lift it generates, consequently if two wins are flying at different speeds the faster wing will have more lift than the slower one. The outside wing in a yaw will therefore have more lift and raise itself up above the inside wing, putting the whole aircraft into a roll. So, just as we get some turning, yawing movement when we bank, so do we get some rolling, banking movement when we yaw. Roll and yaw are linked together. Pitch is the odd one out, for the elevators merely push the nose up or down without any further control effects (apart from the obvious one ot slowing or speeding up the aircraft).

The Axis

One more fact of flight summed all this up. These movements are, to use a technical phrase, 'movements about an axis', (an axis being, to quote the dictionary, 'an imaginary line about which a body rotates'). An aeroplane has three of these imaginary lines. 'Think of them as steel bars stuck through the aircraft like skewers through a joint of beef', said Jeanne.

Axis One is the Lateral Axis, an imaginary steel bar running from wing-tip to wing-tip, along the wings and through the fuselage. The elevators pitch the aircraft round that axis, as we have seen

Axis Two is the Longitudinal Axis, running from nose to tail. The ailerons roll the aircraft round that one.

Axis Three is called the Normal Axis, which runs vertically through the aircraft like a pin stuck through a butterfly. It is the rudder movement which twirls, or yaws, the aircraft round that axis.

By this time Jeanne had drawn a summary of all this on the blackboard.

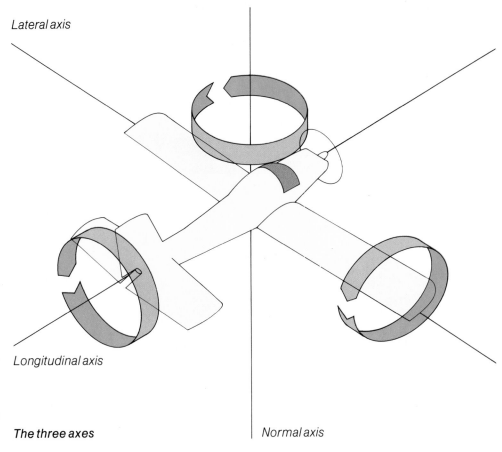

Lateral axis

Longitudinal axis

Normal axis

The three axes

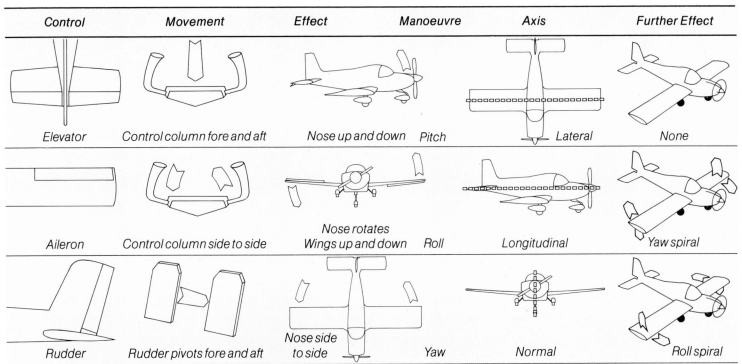

Control	Movement	Effect	Manoeuvre	Axis	Further Effect
Elevator	Control column fore and aft	Nose up and down	Pitch	Lateral	None
Aileron	Control column side to side	Nose rotates Wings up and down	Roll	Longitudinal	Yaw spiral
Rudder	Rudder pivots fore and aft	Nose side to side	Yaw	Normal	Roll spiral

Having copied all that out I, in common, I imagine, with most other students at this stage, began to look out of the window at the line of Cheetah aircraft sitting outside on the taxiway. Would we ever get to the stage of trying all this theory out in the air?

Not yet. There was more talk to come. (Don't worry. These early lessons involve more preliminary talking than the later ones).

Every lesson, apart from teaching a particular movement or flying skill, also imparts a more nebulous concept going under the heading of 'Airmanship'.

Rule One in Airmanship is: 'Keep a Good Lookout.' Every student in every type of flying school will have this dinned in remorselessly. The sky is a big place, but aeroplanes can converge on each other unknowingly in a matter of seconds. Airspace, particularly in the vicinity of airfields where we shall be doing a lot of our training, can get crowded. It is not only a matter of looking where you are going. The whole field of vision has to be scanned for someone coming in your direction. Before making any movement the pilot has to look to see that the bit of sky he is shortly going to occupy is not already occupied — or about to be occupied — by somebody else.

'Don't sit with your nose in the office and let the aircraft plunge around literally in the dark,' said Jeanne. She disliked pilots who flew with what she called 'an inward attitude', staring all the time at instruments, map and the ground. 'Be outgoing. Look around the sky. Keep your head up'.

Elstree, she explained, had no radar. So round the airfield it is the responsibility of pilots to keep away from other aircraft. 'But when you are looking for aeroplanes they are not easy to see. The wings, from ahead or from the side, are so thin that you can't easily make them out against a background of fields, woods or houses. So keep looking out at all times. It is something the examiner will be looking for in the General Flying Test'.

Keep a good look out before any manoeuvre

Trying it out in the air

The second element of airmanship in these early sorties was to know where we were and how to get home again. Most schools and instructors have a pet training area for the first few lessons, a kind of nursery slope. It will have easily recognisable landmarks, be out of other aircraft's way and far from a built up area. We went east, towards the Lee Valley, easily recognisable thanks to huge reservoirs which stand out in the murkiest weather. Epping Forest was also a good landmark, the dark trees standing out well from agricultural land. There was also a light coloured motorway, the M25, leading all the way home.

It is also important that student and instructor should come to an understanding about how to hand over and take over control of the aeroplane from each other. It does not do to have them both tugging at the dual controls together.

'When I say "You have control"', said Jeanne, 'I want you to put your feet lightly on the rudder pedals and your hands lightly on the control column. I don't want you to exert any force on them yet. Then when you are feeling quite happy that you have the aeroplane comfortably at your disposal, you can say: "I have control", and she is all yours.'

'It may be that I will have control but I will want you to follow what I am doing, feeling the movements I am making with hands and feet. I will then say: "Follow me through — on the control column or rudder pedals". That means that your can rest your hands and feet very gently on them, so that you can feel the movements I am making'. We were to do a lot of that, particularly so that I could feel and grow accustomed to the movements of taking off and landing.

Finally, having done our checks and taxied (next Chapter) to the end of the runway we were ready to go. At this stage I had little to do but keep out of the way and take a-hopefully-intelligent interest in what was going on.

I noted the large 09 painted on the tarmac at the beginning of the runway. It meant we were on runway zero nine, so called because it points due east at 90 degrees on the compass rose. (At the other end there is a large 27, because if we were starting from that end we would be going due west, or at 270 degrees. The last digit of these bearings is always missed out, and if that leaves only one figure the convention is to put a makeweight nought in front, as in 09). The picture below shows runway 27 at Elstree.

Down the centre of the tarmac runway stretched a white line. We accelerated straight down the middle of it during the whole take-off, a feat which I was later to discover is much more difficult than it looks. But it was going to be some time yet before I was to be allowed to take the aircraft off.

The figure 27 indicates 270 degrees, runway due west

The Instrument Panel

The galaxy of instruments appears totally confusing at first sight. But gradually the student finds them forming themselves into individual patterns and constellations, each group corresponding to a separate function. Engine gauges in one part, electrical switches in another. The instruments giving us information about the speed, height and attitude of the aircraft are in the most prominent position of all, straight in front of our nose.

With so much else to think about it was no time to begin penetrating the mysteries of the instrument panel. But as we climbed Jeanne pointed out three to watch, the Altimeter, the Airspeed Indicator (ASI) and the Direction Indicator (DI). I watched the large needle on the Altimeter swinging steadily clockwise registering our climb. The needle on the Airspeed Indicator was stuck fast on 85, which was knots, rather than miles per hour. The Direction Indicator needle pointed at a letter E, for east.

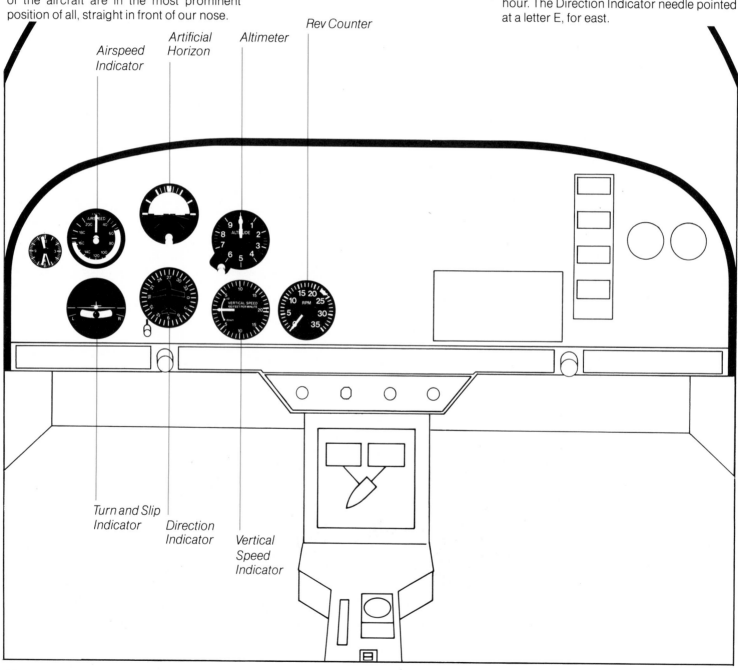

Airspeed Indicator

Artificial Horizon

Altimeter

Rev Counter

Turn and Slip Indicator

Direction Indicator

Vertical Speed Indicator

Pitch

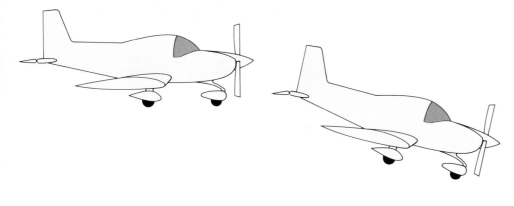

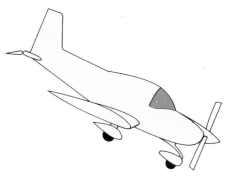

Having reached 2000 feet we went through our exercise. Jeanne demonstrated each one, the pitch, the roll and the yaw, and then it was my turn. 'I have control'. Gingerly edging the column forwards, the ground began to occupy more of the windscreen and there was a sensation of more speed. Edging it back again, the horizon disappeared below the nose. Being careful to hold the wheel lightly with two fingers and thumb I brought her back to something near level flight, after my experiments with pitch.

Looking out from the cabin:

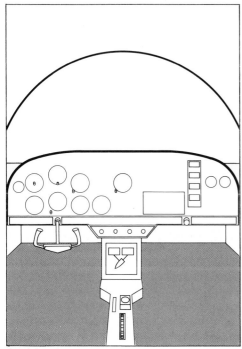

Stick back, nose up

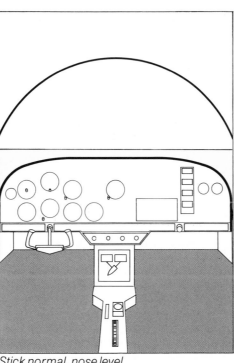

Stick normal, nose level

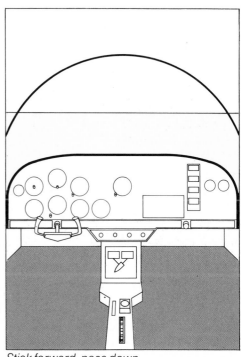

Stick forward, nose down

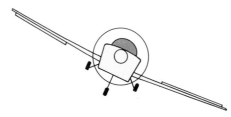
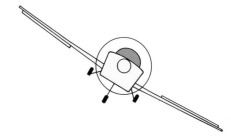

Putting the wheel over to one side will make the aircraft roll in that direction and providing no turn is present, the angle of bank will be proportional to how much you turn the wheel. To level the wings we have to give her some opposite aileron by turning the wheel to the other side, until the wings are level, and then bringing the wheel back to neutral again — in fact, a positive action was needed to change attitude.

Looking out from the cabin:

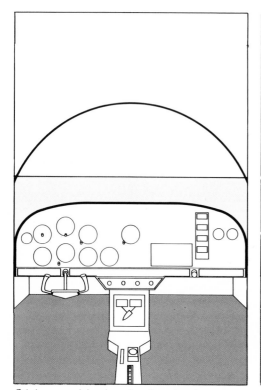
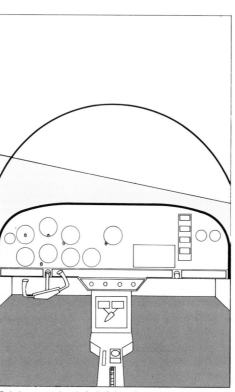
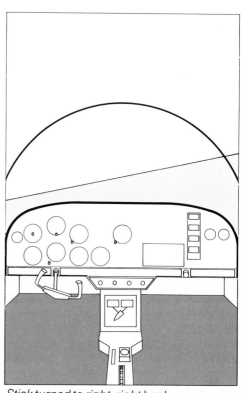

Stick normal, horizon level, no bank   *Stick turned to left, left bank*   *Stick turned to right, right bank*

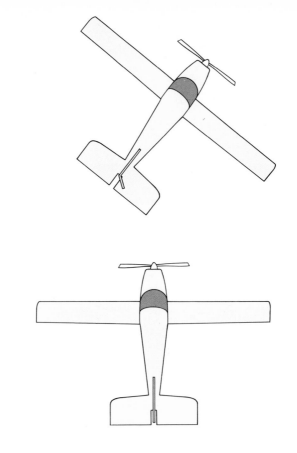

The yaw

Getting the yaw was simply a matter of putting down one foot and holding it there. When the foot came off the aeroplane slewed back into normal flight.

In the beginning I noticed that Jeanne was using the control column and the rudder to stop the 'secondary' effects as I went through the movements. Then, to show the difference, she did nothing, and I experienced the nose coming round in the roll and a wing lifting up in the yaw.

After what seemed about five minutes, but which was more like twenty, we were over the Lee Valley reservoirs, which would prove to be such useful landmarks in the weeks ahead. We turned back westwards and on the way home Jeanne demonstrated the aeroplane's stability by raising the nose and then letting go the control column. The aircraft settled back to level flight in a series of gradually decreasing ups and downs. It inspires confidence to know that when she is properly trimmed she will find her way back to straight and level flight from a dive or from a climb. (She won't level herself from a bank, however. That is up to the pilot).

When the control column was let go, the properly trimmed aircraft gradually settled back to level flight

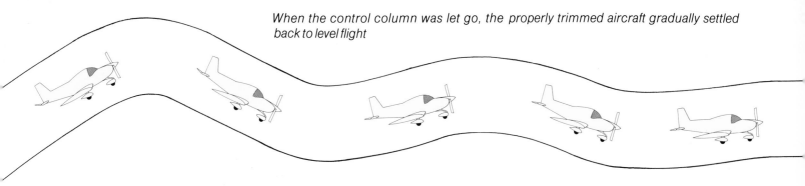

Back on ground and in the operations room a small formality was completed. A dark blue, stiff-backed book was handed to me, bearing the legend in gold print on the cover: *Pilot's Flying Log Book.* Inside, the first printed line was filled out. 'Holder's Operating Capacity: P.U.T.' (Pilot Under Training). 'Journey From: Elstree.' 'To: Elstree.' 'Flying Time: 50 mins.' The first small step into this new world had been taken.

Chapter 4:
Pre-take off checks; and into the air at last!

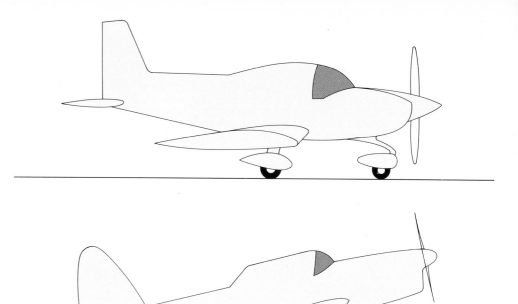

Tricycle and tail wheel undercarriage arrangements

Some things can only be touched on sketchily in the briefing room. The real learning comes from doing them. The process of starting the engine and taxying (moving the aeroplane along the ground) is one of these things. (Why is it called 'taxying'? No one could tell me. 'It always has been'. Presumably a piece of ironic humour from an early aviator, probably French, that caught on).

It was a surprise to be given, right from the start, the task of starting up and taxying to the take-off point. Shoving us in the deep end like this is a deliberate teaching policy which helps to make us feel at home with this unfamiliar piece of machinery. ('Instructors must resist the temptation to take over', says the Elstree teaching notes, 'even when a difficult situation occurs'.)

Taxying is a less demanding business in a modern light aircraft with a tricycle undercarriage (an undercarriage with the third wheel in front) and good disc brakes than it used to be in the older style which had two main wheels and a tail skid, and possibly no brakes at all. ('Tail draggers', as they are called nowadays, particularly by the proud owners and pilots of such aircraft, who tend to feel that handling such a machine is real flying, while tricycle undercarriages are for sissies. Aviation is littered with little pockets of snobbery like this).

The point about a tricycle undercarriage, as fitted to our AA5A, is that it holds the aeroplane in a level attitude on the ground, so that the pilot can see straight ahead over the nose and watch where he is going. The pilot of a 'tail dragger' admittedly has a tougher job: the nose is pointing upwards while he is at rest and taxying. He cannot see straight in front, so he has to weave left and right, looking along the side of the nose to see that the way ahead is clear.

Before we began, Jeanne drew attention to the one trap which practically every novice falls into. Turning on the ground is done with the feet, either the brakes and/or the rudder pedals. It is no use turning the control yoke as though it was the steering wheel of a car and expecting the aircraft to turn. All that does is to work the ailerons, which do practically nothing to the aeroplane taxying along the ground (although, as we shall see, there is something we should do with them when taxying in a high wind). Even after being warned, the instinct to turn the yoke in order to turn the plane on the ground was too strong for me to resist the first time. Everyone is allowed just one of those.

The nose wheels of some types of aircraft are linked with the rudder, so that a certain amount of steering through the swivelling nose wheel is at the pilot's command. But the AA5A does not have this useful aid. It has a free-castering nose wheel, like a supermarket trolley. Steering is done by putting on left or right brakes.

First, I got some general words of advice: 'Aeroplanes are a bit cumbersome on the ground' said Jeanne. 'They are meant to fly, not lumber around down here.' So you have to treat them gently. The speed on the ground is controlled with the throttle, just like the accelerator of a car. It is bad to charge about with too much power and then have to put the brakes on because you are going too fast. That does the tyres and brakes no good. We should taxi with the minimum of power, enough to give us 'a fast walking pace'.

When taxying along the runway itself, far from obstructions or other aeroplanes, then a bit of speed is permissible, even desirable, because the sooner you get out the way and leave the runway clear the better. But out on the taxiway there are aeroplanes on both sides and cars parked as well. There are people walking blithely across the taxiway and a child can dash out between two cars to look at an aeroplane landing. It isn't uncommon to have motorists pull out of the car parking spaces right on front of a passing aeroplane (Rolls-Royce drivers seem particularly prone to do that). An aeroplane at speed can take a bit of stopping. That propeller whirling round up front can do considerable damage. With proper care, taxi accidents should never happen. But they do.

But first, we had to get the engine going. Gone are the days when a faithful mechanic was on hand to speed us away on every flight, checking the machine, putting chocks in front of the wheels, swinging props and standing respectfully to one side as we lords of the air climbed into our flying suits and adjusted our helmets. Having been taken through all the pre-starting checks (see Chapter two) I sat, with check list on my knee, studying the section that is headed STARTING ENGINE.

1 Mixture ... Exercise/set rich

The mixture knob is painted red, just to the right of the throttle. Its job is to vary the mixture of petrol and air, a bit like a choke in a car, but for a different reason. It also works, disconcertingly, in the opposite way. When pulled right out it weakens the mixture to such an extent that an idling engine will be starved of fuel and stop. Pulling it full out (called the 'Idle Cut Off' position) is the usual procedure for stopping the engine, so that we will normally find it pulled out when we come to start up. The drill is to push it and pull once, just to make sure that it works and appears to be connected with its appropriate controls, before pushing it right in to the 'rich' position and leaving it there. (It is coloured red so that you will not confuse it with any other adjacent knobs, like the throttle or cabin heater. It has a second role, enabling us to weaken the mixture, or 'lean it off', when cruising in thinner air at altitude, but more about that later).

2 Throttle ... Exercise/set a quarter inch open

The pilot who shut down the engine will have left this fully out as well. Pushing it fully inwards and out again not only lets you know that it is working on the AA5A it also sends a shot of fuel into the engine to prime the induction which helps to get things going; so don't overdo it or flooding will ensue. How do we judge 'quarter inch open'?

Simply stick your thumb up the shaft of the fully extended throttle until it is about a quarter of an inch from the end, then push the knob in until your thumb meets the nut (called the throttle friction nut) where the throttle disappears into the fascia panel. You have quarter inch open.

3 Engine ... Prime

The primer on the AA5A is the metal knob to the right of the red mixture control knob. Pulling it slowly out and then pressing it smartly in squirts fuel into the cylinders. This is normally done on the first engine start of the day or in particularly cold conditions, when it would be normal to use some choke on a car engine. Just how much priming an engine needs is a matter of personal experience and the climate (about two pushes of the primer seem normal for the first start on the AA5A).

Having primed, we need to get a move on and start her up, so

4 Propeller ... Clear

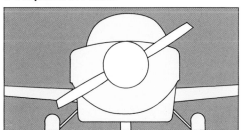

Make sure there is nobody loitering around the propeller and also inform everyone within earshot that you are about to start up by

sliding back the canopy and shouting 'Clear Prop!', much in the manner of a golfer shouting 'Fore!' before he drives off. I found this a slightly self-conscious procedure, particularly when shouting to an apparently empty world. But the day may come when it will stop you slicing someone in half.

5 Magneto Switch ... On Left

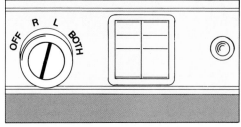

Your keys will be lying on top of the instrument panel. Put the appropriate one in the ignition lock, called for historic reasons, the magneto switch, in memory of the time when each of the two magnetos had its own tumbler switch, like ordinary electric light switches. Larger aircraft still do. The key can be moved to four positions, OFF, R, L, BOTH.

This is, perhaps, the time to explain that for safety and efficiency aeroplane engines have two separate magnetos, each providing sparks to one of two plugs in each cylinder. The safety aspect of this is obvious. If one magneto packs up you will have one complete ignition system left to keep the engine running. In an aero engine, which has large cylinders and roomy combustion chambers, two sparks burn more of the petrol/air mixture than one. So it is more efficient. Just how efficient you can check for yourself, by switching from both magnetos to one and seeing how the engine revs will drop. For starting the Cheetah we move the key to L (for left) rather than BOTH, which also needs some explaining. There is no such thing as a neutral gear in an aircraft, so that when the starter turns the engine it has to turn everything else, including the hefty propeller. This is a big load for a twelve volt battery. It means that the engine turns quite slowly, much more slowly than the normal car engine when the starter is pressed. It grinds away in a quite lugubrious and painful manner. The problem is to ensure that in spite of this slow rotation the magneto will deliver a spark of sufficient power and kick to get the engine going. There are various ways of solving this difficulty. The AA5A has a special High Intensity Magneto on the left hand side, designed to give a good spark at low speeds. So we start on L, left mag, and don't switch to BOTH until she is firing. Key to L, therefore.

We now arrive at a part of the check list with a black line down the left hand side. This means that it should be learnt by heart. The object is to enable us to keep our head up and look round to see what is happening while going through the check items, rather than having to keep our heads buried in the script. Starting the engine turns the aircraft from a static object into a live and lethal thing. Someone absorbed in reading the check list might not realise that the brakes were not holding and that the aircraft was moving before the propeller started to chew up another parked aircraft.

Learning things by heart is a problem for many people. But it becomes easier if there is some kind of story involved, some rational explanation for the things which have to be remembered and the order in which they occur. When looked at logically, this part of the list makes sense.

6 Starter . . . Operate

Obviously the next move. On the AA5A it's a button to the left of the throttle. While pressing it with the left thumb it is good policy to have the right hand resting on the throttle, ready to close it completely if need be, while the feet hover over the brakes ready to come down on them hard if the parking brake is not holding. It is a 'ready for anything' attitude which will come as second nature after a while. It is pointless to go on churning away on the starter if there is no sign of life. It will rapidly run the battery down. She may be flooded with too much fuel, in which case giving her a few turns with the throttle fully open and the mixture pulled out to the weakest 'leaned off' position will help clear her. Or she may be not rich enough, in which case another prime or a pump on the throttle

should help. Aeroplane engines can be temperamental. They all have their quirks and habits which only experience will teach.

7 Starter Warning Light . . . Off

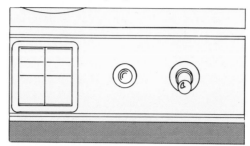

On the AA5A a small light to the left of the starter button glows while the starter is being worked and is drawing current from the aircraft battery.

After she fires and the starter is released the very first thing to notice is that the light has gone off. If it hasn't it is likely to mean that the starter hasn't disengaged or that the alternator is not working. In either case the engine has to be shut down. There is no point in going on until the fault has been traced and cured.

8 Brakes . . . Holding

Obviously the next thing to look for. If the parking brake doesn't seem to be holding her, the two toe brakes will have to be applied while you have another push and pull at the parking brake.

9 Magneto Switch . . . On BOTH

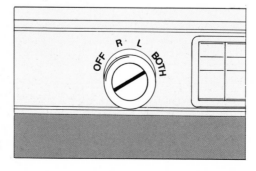

Having checked for the potentially immediately damaging things it's time to get the engine going properly, using both ignition systems. At this point I should confess that I have sometimes found it possible to persuade an unenthusiastic engine into life (one that was churning over on the starter with the occasional splutter but just failing to catch properly) by switching to BOTH a bit early. No one seemed to mind.

10 Oil Pressure . . . Check

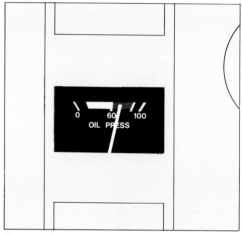

By now the needle of the oil pressure gauge, grouped with the other engine gauges over on the right hand side of the instrument panel, should have moved up into the green arc on the dial, which signifies its normal working pressure. If it isn't 'in the green' something is wrong with the engine or the oil system. Close down at once before the engine is damaged.

11 Throttle . . . 1200 RPM

Having made sure that we have got oil pressure we can bring the engine speed up to a useful warming up level, 1200 revs per minute in the case of the AA5A. It also ensures that we are generating electric current for the radios, etc. We check the rev counter to see that we have got that engine speed. We should then carry on looking over to the right to make sure that other vital bits of the system are all working.

12 Fuel Pressure ... Check

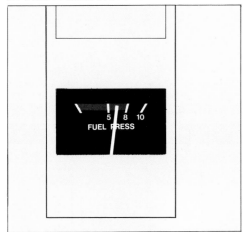

If all is well the needle of the fuel pressure gauge should be somewhere in the middle of the green arc of the dial, showing that the fuel is being happily fed under pressure from the tanks to the carburettor. If it isn't it could mean one of several things: you have forgotten to switch the fuel on; you are running on an empty tank; the fuel pump is not working, something which can found out by switching on the auxiliary electrical fuel pump and seeing if it makes any difference to the pressure; or there is simply a blockage. By this time the engine will probably have spluttered into silence in any case. But having noted the lack of fuel pressure you will at least know where to start looking for the trouble that stopped you.

13 Alternator ... Check

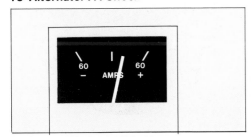

If the alternator is not doing its job providing the power to run the electrics, the ammeter needle (top of the engine gauges on the right) will be well in the 'minus' region, showing that the battery is bearing the load. If the alternator *doesn't* appear to be working, check first that it is switched on. The alternator switch (grouped with the master switch to the right of the magneto switch) is quite delicate and can sometimes be clicked off by mistake in the general flurry of starting. If it isn't that, then the proposed flight will have to be abandoned until the problem is solved, for the alternator is your primary source of electric power. You can take comfort from the fact that the fault happened while you were still on the ground.

14 Suction ... Check

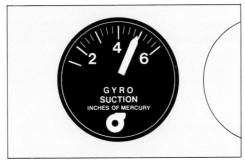

Two important instruments, the Director Indicator (DI) and the Artificial Horizon are worked by gyroscopes driven by vacuum power. (A small chat about what the gyros do and how comes later). The vacuum is created by a pump driven by the engine. The Suction Gauge, on the far upper right of the AA5A's instrument panel, reveals whether the vacuum is working. The needle should be in the middle, between 4.6 and 5.4 on the dial. If it isn't, this aeroplane is not for you.

That completes the Engine Starting Checks. Describing them makes it sound a plodding, laborious business. With time they become a smooth, rapid routine. The skill is to go through them speedily, but without losing thoroughness. If you want to practice you can always play at make-believe engine start-ups in the car!

We are now sitting in a happy, shuddering, functioning aeroplane. But before moving off there are still things to be done, now that we know that the engine is providing us with the electrical power to do them.

It is a new section of the Check List, headed ...

After Engine Start

1 Radio/Nav Aids/Intercom ... On

It is time to turn the radio knob to 'on', reach for the headset with attached microphone and make sure that instructor and student can talk to each other and hear each other. 'Nav Aids' are the various radio navigational instruments, the working of which will come later. At this stage we have enough to think about without them. The various small switches and control boxes which go with an aircraft's radio communication and navigation system vary from plane to plane, and can be quite complex. I once spent five minutes sitting on the ground in one lavishly equipped machine hunting for the right combination of switches to make the radio work. At the monstrous rate I was paying for that aircraft, it added up to nearly £4 worth of frustration, so it is useful to get a guided tour of the avionics (as all the bits of radio gear are called) early on. Use of the volume control on the radio will enable instructor and student to talk to each other in normal conversational tones. (Make sure your mouth-piece is near your mouth, not by your nose, where it will pick up unnecessary heavy breathing).

2 Magnetos ... Check

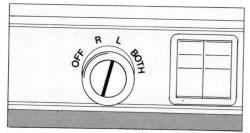

It is just a matter of testing that they are all working, and also that the 'Off' position is working, so that you can shut off quickly in an emergency. You need a quick turn of the switch to the left through all positions and back to BOTH. The engine should give a slight hiccough as you pass in and out of 'Off'.

3 Flaps ... Check/set up

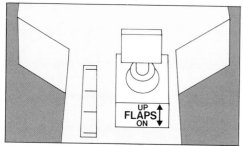

Now that we have got some power we can test the flaps without straining the battery, for on the AA5 these are electrically operated. The flap switch is between the seats. Pulling it back and holding it there brings the flaps down. Have a look to see that they are both coming down. Pushing the switch forward will bring them up again. One of the helpful points about this switch is that there is a fully forward position in which it will stay of its own accord, bringing the flaps up while the pilot gets on with something else. Make sure they have come up. (The check lists of some aircraft require the flaps to be put down right at the beginning of the checks, before the engine has started. This certainly helps with the inspection of the flap mechanism, but it does take power from the battery. I have noticed that pilots, even of these aircraft, sometimes prefer to wait until they have got the engine going. Aviators treat their batteries tenderly).

4 Nav Aids ... Check/Set
Once again, something for later in our career. Though I noticed Jeanne doing things to little boxes at this stage.

5 Radio ... Check/Call

This is our first step in the daunting business of Radiotelephony, or R/T, which is nowadays a key element in learning to fly. At the beginning the whole thing sounds like a foreign language, moreover, made up largely of numerals. But slowly comprehension dawns. It is mostly a question of speaking well-rehearsed lines and receiving predictable responses. This first pre-taxying call is a way of giving the student a gentle introduction, like playing First Lord in *Hamlet*. (We shall go into the refinements of R/T in a later chapter). The main rules are to wait until no one else is speaking and to keep it short. 'Terseness' is the R/T byword. After a bit it becomes fun and you will find yourself slipping into the languid, fluent, world-weary tone affected by British Airways captains and test pilots.

With this first message we are finding out whether the radio is working and, simultaneously, asking for clearance to taxi, telling the air traffic controller who we are and what we are proposing to do, and collecting vital information about which runway is in use and how we should set our altimeter.

So we wait for a gap, (other people's talk will help us get the volume right, though most radios have a test position which gives a hiss enabling you to adjust according to the loudness of the hiss) press the transmit button on the control column (or on our hand microphone, if one of those is being used) and deliver the following:

'Elstree, this is Golf Bravo Golf Victor Whisky, pre-flight check and taxi clearance, captain's name McCabe, plus one, to the east.'

Then, don't forget to let go of the button.

Back will come something like this:

'Victor Whisky, hearing you fives, runway two seven, with left hand circuit, noise abatement departure, the QFE is one zero zero ninah, with a QNH one zero two zero.'

What does it all mean?

He is telling us that he is hearing us strength five in a readability scale stretching from one (unreadable) to five (perfectly readable), so

that's all right. Secondly, we now know that runway 27 is the runway in use, i.e. the one pointing towards 270 degrees, due west. 'Left hand circuit' means that the circuit pattern in use at the airfield (more about that when we get to circuits) goes to the left after take-off. 'Noise abatement departure' is a reminder that there is a special rule in force at Elstree for the benefit of the long suffering people living at the end of runway 27, which holds that we should swing to the right immediately after becoming airborne to avoid climbing over their roofs on full power. The QFE and the QNH are matters which we will come to when we are investigating altimeters (Chapter six). Suffice to know that as we are leaving the circuit we shall be setting our altimeter to the QNH, which means that it will register the altitude above mean sea level. One zero two zero refers to the present atmospheric pressure, 1020 millibars. By twiddling the small knob protruding from the bottom left of the Altimeter in front of us we can get 1020 to appear opposite the arrow in the window on the right hand side of the dial. This will leave the Altimeter registering 330 feet, which happens to be the height of Elstree above sea level, so we got that right. But before doing that, there is a bit more R/T procedure to go through. One of the rules of the game is that every time we are given directions or numbers we should repeat them back to demonstrate that we have heard them correctly. So we reply with something like:

'Two Seven Left, QNH One Zero Two Zero and QFE One Zero Zero Ninah. Victor Whisky.' (Note that we end with our own call sign, to show him that it is us talking).

If there is then silence, we got it right and can then proceed. If we got it wrong he will say so and repeat the right information, after which we will repeat it back to him, correctly this time, we hope.

6 Flight Instruments ... Check/Set
Having got the Altimeter setting we need we can now set it, as described above. We can also press and turn the knob at the bottom left of the Direction Indicator (DI) and move it round until it shows the same reading opposite the arrow at the top of the dial as the compass situated above our head at the top of the windscreen. (We shall have more

to say about the habits of the DI later). As for the other instruments, there is nothing much in the way of checking we can do at this stage, beyond noting that they are there, and that their glass faces are intact (which, as we shall see later, is important).

We are now ready to go. Having had a good look to see that no one else is coming along the taxi path in our direction and that the way is clear, we push in the parking brake, check that it has released, feet on the toe brakes and open the throttle slightly to get ourselves moving. If the aeroplane was parked on grass it may need quite a bit of power to get it going. On one soggy day it needed a combination of high revs plus a rhythmic backwards and forwards motion of the control column which set the plane rocking gently, thanks to the action of the slipstream on the elevators which eased the nose up and down and helped unstick the nose wheel. (You have to be careful not to rock the propeller into the ground, however).

Having got her moving there is one vital check to be made straight away: will the brakes stop her if necessary? We test them after the first few yards by bringing down the engine revs and putting our feet gently but firmly on the brakes. In the beginning I used to stamp hard on the brakes and bring the aircraft to a lunging halt until it was pointed out to me that this brutal handling was unnecessary. The instructor has a set of brakes which need to be tested as well, so having got on the move again the drill is to hand over ('you have control') and let the instructor have a go.

The famous 'fast walking pace' came with about 1000 revs on the tarmac in the AA5A. But one bad habit I got into was to stick the throttle at 1000 revs and control the speed purely with the brakes, using them to slow down in a downhill bit or when approaching a corner. That's wrong. It is making the brakes work against the power, which is wearing them out unnecessarily. The correct method is to use the throttle, bringing the power back for slowing down and increasing it momentarily for hills or rough grassy patches. The brakes may have to be used as well, of course, but at least they won't be fighting against the power. The throttle friction nut, which is the knurled ring at the base

of the throttle, can be screwed anti-clockwise to make the throttle quite slack and easy to push and pull during taxying. (During the pre-take-off checks it will be tightened up again to stop it vibrating backwards and reducing the power setting during a take-off or climb).

There is a right angle turn to the left in the taxiway on the trip to the runway at Elstree. It doesn't do to corner too fast, so the procedure is to slow down slightly before the turn, then put on gradual left brake, adding a bit of power to help her round. Avoid locking the wheel and screwing round on the tyre. It is both bad for the tyre cover and puts an unnecessary strain on the u/c leg. Ahead now lies the entry to the runway, but before that a white line is drawn across the taxiway. We do not go beyond that point without the permission of the control tower. But there is no point in wasting everyone's time and asking for permission if somebody is about to use the runway for a take-off or landing. So we have a good look over to the end of the runway and beyond to the approach. If no one is in sight we take to the dreaded R/T again with a short, snappy request to enter the runway and backtrack along it to the end, which goes something like this:

'Victor Whisky, ready to backtrack.'

If we are lucky we will get back:

'Victor Whisky, clear backtrack'.

Actually, it will probably sound more like 'Trawisky, clabbertrap'. But you will get used to that kind of thing. You then acknowledge with your call sign to show that you have understood; provided, of course, that you really have.

'Victor Whisky'.

According to a government publication called *CAP 46, Radio Telephony Procedure,* obtainable from HM Stationery Office (which everyone is advised to buy), the radio exchanges I have just reproduced are not strictly in accordance with the rules. Messages expecting a reply are supposed to end with the word 'over'. Messages ending a conversation are supposed to finish with the word 'out'. A message agreeing to comply

with some advice or instruction is supposed to include the handy word 'wilco'. But although neither CAP 46 nor any other book of instruction I have read admits it, these things are commonly dropped in the everyday hurly-burly of round-the-home-airfield chat. It may also come about that you will hear yourself being given clearance to enter the runway and backtrack before you have even asked for it. In many airfields, including Elstree, you pass in front of the eyes of the gent in the tower while taxying out to the runway, so he may help you on your way by anticipating your call. So when, while thinking of something else, you suddenly hear your earphones say 'Victor Whisky, clear to backtrack', you just acknowledge with 'Victor Whisky' and get on with it (having first had a good look to make sure that it really is clear). After a while you develop the ability to react as though the telephone bell had rung when in the midst of the burble of all the other talk your own call sign impinges on your consciousness.

Apart from the brakes, there is one other check that needs to be done during taxying.

7 Flight Instruments . . . Check

While moving along the ground we can check that *some* of the instruments which tell us how the aircraft is moving are working. By turning to the left we should provoke an appropriate response from the Turn and Slip Indicator, the Direction Indicator and the Compass. The needle of the Turn and Slip Indicator on the bottom row left of the panel will show a left turn, while the spirit-level-like black ball at the bottom of the dial will lunge over to the right, showing that we are indulging in a nasty flat turn on the ground rather than a well balanced aerial one (when the ball, as we shall discover later, should remain in the middle). The DI and the Compass should move in the correct direction with our turns, but the instruments showing height changes (the Vertical Speed Indicator, the Artificial Horizon, the Altimeter) should naturally all stay put. Some instructors recommend a quick zig-zag while taxying to test these things. I conscientiously went through this routine during my general flying test, only to be told that I was wasting my time. Hadn't I already turned left and right in the normal course of taxying? Why didn't I simply use those turns to check the instruments.

Effects of wind on control surfaces when taxying

Wind can cause problems while taxying. A strong side wind hitting the fin at the rear will try to weather-cock the machine round, nose into wind. A touch of opposite brake may be needed to stop that. Ailerons can be used to keep a wing down when the wind is from the side, threatening to get under the wing surface and keel the plane over.

Later in my taxying career it was pointed out to me that countering the effect of wind on the ground can become quite complex, depending on where the wind is coming from. Common sense, plus a bit of working out, will show that the effect of the ailerons when the wind is coming from slightly behind the aircraft will be the reverse of the normal situation, when the airflow is coming from ahead. It is therefore no use putting on the equivalent of left bank to stop the left wing lifting if a strong, gusty breeze is blowing from behind your left ear. The airflow will merely meet the upturned left aileron and find a bit more leverage to work on rather than less. So it is wise to keep an eye on the windsock beside the runway and be aware all the time where the wind is coming from in relation to the direction you are taxying. The rule about keeping the stick well back to keep the weight off the nose wheel will also not apply if you are taxying before a strong following wind. In that case pushing the control column forward will do the trick. Just to make it all more complicated, you must remember to bring the stick back again if you apply more power for some reason, because that will create a slipstream from the propeller which will cancel out the wind. When one remembers that this all becomes more vital for 'tail draggers', who have to be on their guard against having the aeroplane blown on its nose and catching the propeller

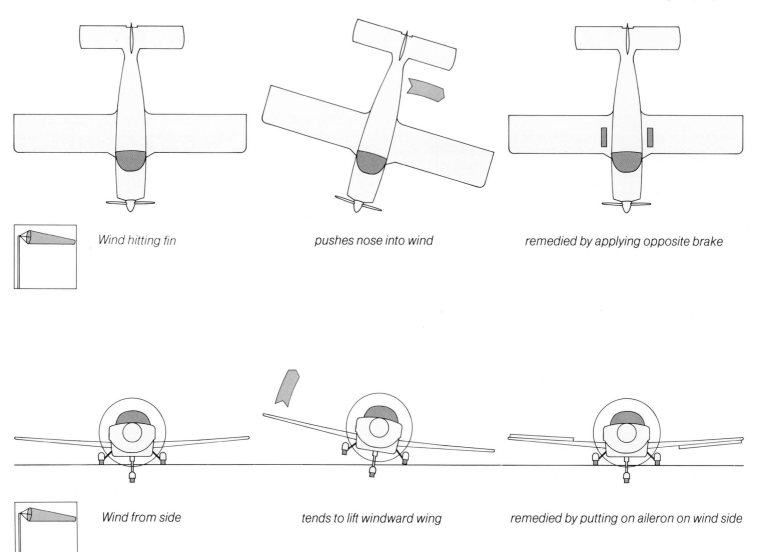

Wind hitting fin

pushes nose into wind

remedied by applying opposite brake

Wind from side

tends to lift windward wing

remedied by putting on aileron on wind side

while weaving about looking where they are going, one begins to feel a bit more sympathy for their feelings of superiority.

'Supposing', said Jeanne, 'that you found that the brakes had suddenly stopped working while you were taxying. What do you do?'

'Ah, yes, well. Close the throttle and let her come to a stop of her own accord. Perhaps turning onto some grass or facing uphill to help halt her . . .'

'And how are you going to turn, with no brakes and no slipstream to act on the rudder? Supposing you were on the taxiway, going slightly downhill, between a corridor of aeroplanes and cars which didn't leave you any room to turn and there was another aeroplane which had stopped in front of you . . .'

'Help. Got to stop that propeller'.

That was, sort of, the answer. Drag the idle cut-off (red mixture knob) out, turn off the fuel (so that we are less likely to start a fire if we do hit anything), put the ignition switch to 'off' and turn off the master switch, which cuts off all the electrics and reduces the chance of any sparks. Then get ready to leave (canopy unlatched and open).

Our destination for a take-off from runway 27 is a large sunken concrete dish at the end of the runway proper called 'the Pan'. This is where aircraft do their pre-take-off checks and queue up waiting to be given permission to move up to the runway proper for their take off. The concrete in this bit of Elstree is quite rough and as the entry is downhill, we need to reduce power and take it slowly after our quick sprint along the runway to reach it.

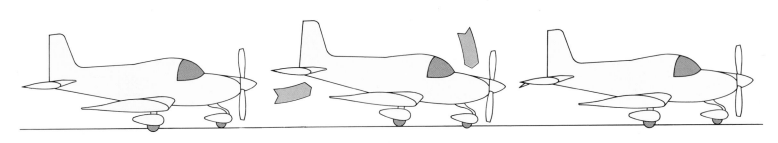

Wind from behind tends   *to lift tailplane*   *remedied by pulling stick back to lift nose*

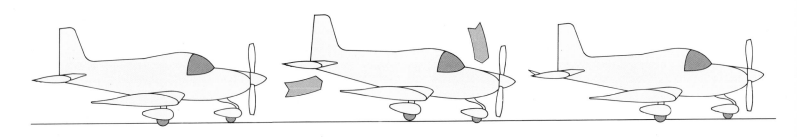

Wind from behind   *tends to lift tailplane*   *more power, stronger slipstream, cancels wind*

43

The power check

The next task is to carry out what is called the Power Check. This involves opening the throttle and running the engine up to 1800 revs while checking that everything is as it should be. To do this we swing the aircraft round facing the wind, at the same time tucking ourselves into one side of 'the Pan' or the other so that we don't put off anyone coming in over our heads to land. A piece of stylish perfection is to run forward a few paces having completed our swing round, so that we straighten the nosewheel, which will allow us to make a quick, straight departure without sideways strain on the nosewheel when the time comes to go. Then we bring the revs back to 1200 RPM, put the parking brake on and get on with the Power Checks.

Once more, these are checks which need to be memorised, so that we can give all our attention to what is happening in and out of the cockpit. The fact that we are going to put quite a bit of power on makes it all the more important that we should not have our head buried in the check list. But having finished, have a quick glance through to make sure you haven't missed anything.

1 Temperatures and Pressures ... Check
The famous 'Ts and Ps'. It doesn't do to rev an engine up until the oil has warmed up (cold, glutinous oil is a bad lubricator). So we need to check that the oil temperature gauge over on the right has had time to edge up into the green part of the dial. Give it a bit longer at 'warming-up' revs if it hasn't. Of course, you also need to see that the temperature hasn't shot up to the hot end of the dial, an indication that something serious is wrong, probably a leak. At the same time the oil pressure needs a glance, and fuel pressure.

2 Fuel Selector ... Fullest Tank
We had chosen the emptiest tank to taxi over here. We are now going for the fullest tank for the take-off. To make absolutely certain that fuel is running freely from this tank, and that it won't suddenly peter out as we take off, we switch tanks now, before running up the engine. That period of trial will reveal any blockage. One of the rules: never take off with a newly switched-on, untried tank. It's like sending in an unknown batsman to open the cricket match.

3 Throttle ... 1800 RPM
Before doing it, have a look round behind, because you are going to create quite a draught. Make sure you are not going to subject another aircraft, or even family picnickers, to the blast. If need be, you can point the aircraft a few degrees in another direction as long as you don't go too far off the direction of the wind. Don't shove the throttle open with a lunge, forcing the engine to cope with sudden stresses. Ease it gently.

4 Carburettor Heat ... Check
We met this in the pre-starting checks. Now is the time to see if it is working. When pulled out (to 'hot') we should see the engine revs drop slightly. Why? Because hot air is being directed through the carburettor into the cylinders. Hot air being less dense than cold air a less punchy charge is being delivered into the combustion chambers. Hence the drop in revs. Having noted the rev drop,

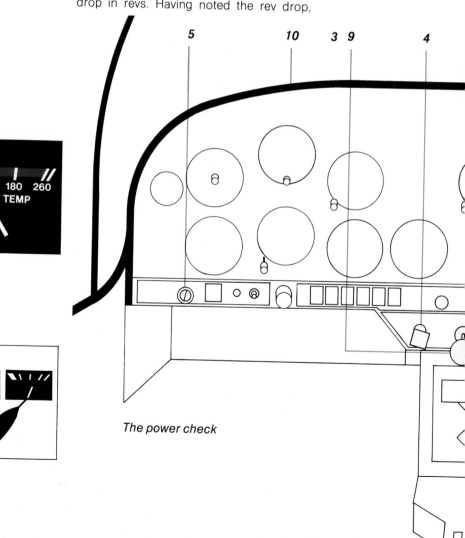

The power check

push it back in again. It is just possible, of course, that ice could have formed in the carburettor during taxying. Starting up and taxying over wet, dewy grass on a keen morning is one of the easiest ways to draw moisture up into the carburettor where it is subjected to ice-forming pressure and temperature drops. In such a case, various things can happen when the carburettor heat is pulled out. The most likely is that the engine will first get rougher and slower as lumps of ice are dislodged and sucked into the cylinders, eventually picking up to smoother, higher revs than were set before the carb heat test. The lesson about being careful of the morning dew will then have been learned.

5 Magnetos... Check

Now is the time to find out how each of our two ignition systems is working at these higher revs. The key is turned from the

BOTH position right across to L for left. By watching the rev counter we should see a drop of not more than about 150 revs, as each cylinder goes onto one sparking plug rather than two. Then back to BOTH and over again to R, to test the right magneto system. Again the drop should be not more than about 150 revs, and according to the handbook should not differ from the other system by more than 75 revs.

6 Temperatures and Pressures... Check

Another look over to the right to see that the high revs haven't caused any problems.

7 Alternator... Check

While paying attention to the right hand gauges we look up to see that we are still getting a healthy + charge on the Ammeter.

8 Suction... Check

Without it the Artificial Horizon and the turn needle will not work.

9 Throttle... Close—check—idle—set 1200 RPM

It is a matter of pulling the throttle back slowly and gently until it won't come back any further. At that stage the engine should be ticking over at 500 to 600 revs. Don't keep it there too long, but gently increase again to our 1200 RPM setting. You are checking that she will idle nicely in the glide.

10 I/F Screens... As required

If we are doing some instrument flying training, which we shall be later on, this would be the time to erect the special cage of screens which act as blinkers round the trainee instrument flyer.

Having done all that, there only remains the vital actions before take-off and we can actually think about leaving.

The engine and instrument systems are working well enough to take us into the air. What comes next is a last check round the aeroplane plus one or two things which need to be done to prepare for the take-off.

For this the check list can be read. I found myself mouthing the words as I touched the various instruments and controls which needed to be set or checked. This is apparently not a bad way of doing it.

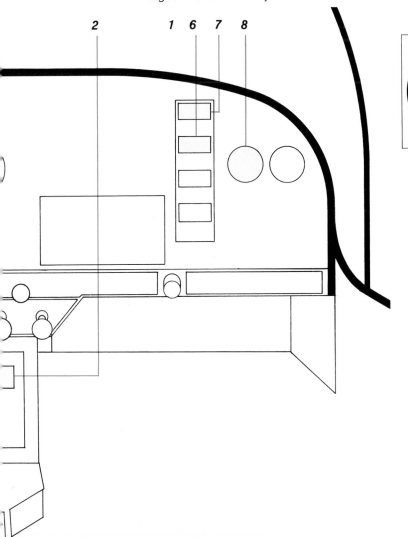

Pre-take off

1 Trimmer ... Set

The trim wheel, which is discussed in Chapter five, should be set to neutral, so that the small pointer is by the centre line on the indicator beside it.

2 Throttle Friction ... Set

Having finished with taxying we now tighten up the knurled ring, so that the throttle control stays put, particularly when it needs to remain at 'full throttle' during the take-off and climb.

3 Mixture ... Rich

It always has to be pushed right in at its rich position when using full throttle to take off and climb.

4 Carburettor Heat ... Cold

That needs to be pushed right in for full throttle work as well.

5 Fuel Selector ... On/Contents

Is the fuel still turned on and is the tap pointing to the fullest tank, which shows enough fuel to get us to where we want to go? Is the electric fuel pump on as an insurance against mechanical pump failure?

6 Primer ... Locked

A yank at the metal primer knob to make sure the locking pin is engaged.

7 Magnetos ... BOTH

After all our twiddling of the magneto switch we need to make sure that we have got them both on now.

8 Flaps ... Set

For take-off the book says the AA5A should be given one third flap. So we press the flap switch until the indicator has reached the first (or one third) mark, having a look outside to see that they have, in fact, come down.

9 Engine Gauges ... Check

A look over to the right to see that the temperatures, pressures, suction and current are still as they should be.

10 Cabin Heat/Ventilation ... Set

Pulling out the cabin heat knob in the centre of the panel will give warm air. Small knobs at bottom left and right of the panel, when pulled, will give pilot and/or passenger a cold draught up their sleeves.

11 Flashing Beacon ... On

It should have been on from just after starting the engine, because we don't taxi around the aerodrome without it. Airliners put it on before, but light 'plane batteries are very small and they need all the current for the starter. This is just to check that it hasn't got itself switched off.

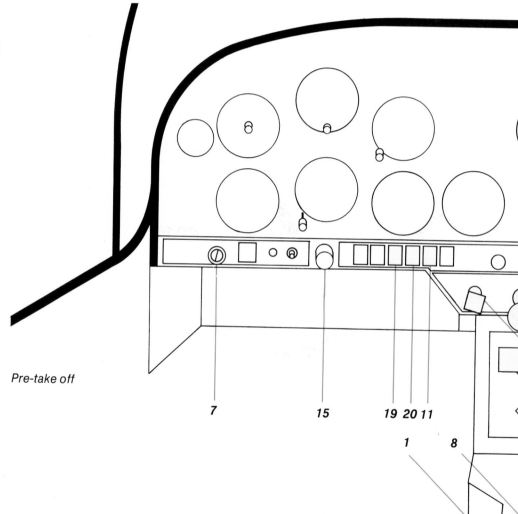

Pre-take off

12 Auto Pilot ... Off

If we have got one, we make sure it is switched off. It is a useful aid when cruising, allowing the pilot to turn his mind to other problems while a gyroscope and some hydraulic pumps fly the aeroplane. But for taking off, *we* fly.

13 Seat Belts and Shoulder Straps ... Secure

Is everyone strapped in tightly? Don't forget the passengers behind, if any.

14 Canopy ... Locked

Give it a tug backwards to see that it won't fly open.

15 Flying Controls . . . Free

This is a test to make sure that no bits of stone or other obstructions have lodged in the controls on the way over, or that nothing else has occurred to jam them, such as (to quote the experience of a friend) a wind-blown twig getting itself jammed in the elevator. The idea is to move the control column to its extremes; as far forward as it will go, simultaneously giving it full right and left movement, then as far back as it will go, giving it the same aileron treatment. Then, try full left and right rudder as well.

16 Flight Instruments . . . Check

Is the Direction Indicator still in tune with the compass? Is the altimeter fixed on the right setting and is it still making sense, i.e. showing roughly zero if it is set to the aerodrome QFH, or the correct height if it is set to sea level QNH?

17 Airways Departure Clearance . . . As required

Not for us at this stage. But if we were flying along the recognised controlled corridors (which we shall meet later) called Airways, this is where we would get our precise instructions about height, direction and who to report to from air traffic control. Occasionally, while waiting one's turn to potter round the circuit, one hears some maestro in a twin turbo-prop getting his instructions for departure to Geneva or somewhere, and one can dream of days to come.

18 Radio/Nav Equipment . . . Set

Also not for us at this stage.

19 Pitot Heater . . . On if icing conditions are present

During take-off getting correct airspeed readings is vital. We could have just picked up enough moisture or rain in the taxying and take-off run to form ice when it meets a strong, cool airstream, which could interfere with the airspeed indicated at a vital moment.

20 Strobes . . . On

If you've got strobe lights fitted as an extra, bung them on so that everyone can see you flashing your way down the runway and into the sky. In aircraft not fitted with them a curious, homely convention appears to have grown up among certain pilots, who will solemnly deliver the monologue 'We haff no strobes' in whatever accent they feel like at the time, from Orstrylian to Boris Karloff. It is a handy finale to the pre-take-off checks.

Now, having turned the aircraft slightly to check visually whether anyone is coming in to land, and having found that they aren't, you can let the controller know that you would like to go.

'Victor Whisky, ready for take off.'

The response could be:

'Victor Whisky, clear take off.'

Or:

'Victor Whisky, line up and hold.'

Which means that there is probably somebody on the runway at the moment. But you can get on out of 'the Pan' and stop on the lines ('piano keys') at the end of the runway until you get:

'Victor Whisky, clear take off.'

Then, it's:

'Victor Whisky, rolling.'

And having had a quick look to see that your DI and Compass are pointing roughly at 270 (the way you are taking off) and that the engine temperatures and pressures are still healthy, away you go. Exactly how, we'll come to later.

18   9   14

5   4   2   3   10   6

Chapter 5
New puzzles: the use of flaps and power

I had learnt what using the elevators, rudder and ailerons did to the aeroplane. The next session examined the other two controls:
1 Altering the power (using the throttle)
2 Using the flaps.

But before getting up in the air I was introduced to three items which come under the general heading of 'Airmanship'.

The Clock Code

1 The convention of the Clock Code. 'If you see another aeroplane while we are up there don't just point it out to me by sticking your finger at it and saying "there's an aeroplane"', said Jeanne. Instead we use the clock code, which is probably already familiar to most people. The sky is divided up like the face of a clock, with the nose of the aircraft pointing to twelve o'clock. Three o'clock is the right (starboard) wing, six the tail, and nine the left wing. Fill in the other hours for the bits in between. If the object sighted is above the horizon you add 'high'; on the horizon is 'level', below it is 'low'. Now we know what those wartime aces shouting 'Bandits twelve o'clock high' were trying to tell us.

The clock code

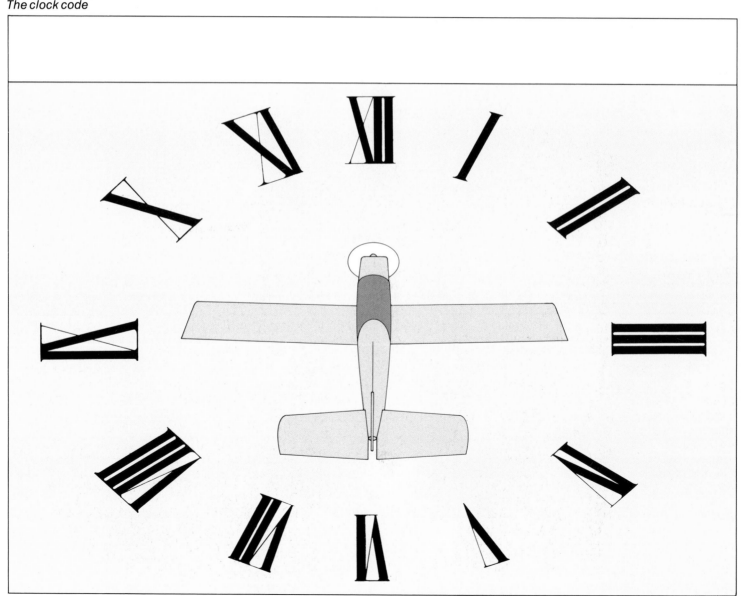

Flap limiting speed

2 As we shall be using flaps we need to know about the concept of Flap Limiting Speed. All aircraft have a speed above which flaps should not be lowered, for fear of harming the flap mechanism or even, in an extreme case, ripping them off. If we were to put an arm outside the cockpit at something over 100 mph airspeed we should discover just what kind of a force the flaps have to meet when they are lowered. They are large objects and a close look at them will show that the hinges which attach them to the

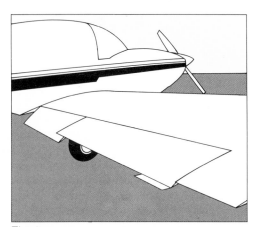

The flap

airframe take quite a beating. In the AA5A Cheetah the maximum speed at which flaps can be lowered is 103 knots. As a helpful aid that speed is shown on the airspeed indicator, which has a number of coloured arcs running round the outside of the face between certain of the numerals, each colour having a certain meaning.

The arc referring to the flaps is the white one, stretching between 53 kts and 104 kts. We must always ensure that we have the speed within that white arc before working the flap switch. (And, naturally, if the flaps are down we must never put the nose down and pile on power so that the airspeed needle climbs beyond the arc).

What about the other colours?

The green arc is the Normal Operating Range, stretching from 55–150 kts on the Cheetah. Within that range there are no particular problems about using the controls

(apart, of course, from the flaps) although it is advisable not to do anything too violent with them at the top end of that range except in an emergency manoeuvre to get out of someone's way.

The yellow arc is the Caution Range, from 130–165 kts. If you are going to use the controls at this speed, use them gently, slowly, carefully, to avoid putting undue stresses on the aircraft.

The red line at 164 kts shows the Never Exceed speed. That marks the no-go area.

The airspeed indicator

(It is commonly called the Vne, Velocity Never Exceed). Using the controls above that speed may distort them or damage the airframe itself. Bits may start falling off. What happens if we find ourselves inadvertently screaming down in a dive at 164 kts or above? We have got to get rid of the speed.

As a start we can take off any power that we have got on, which should make a big difference. In an emergency something would have to be gently moved, of course. But the idea is not to get into such a position in the first place.

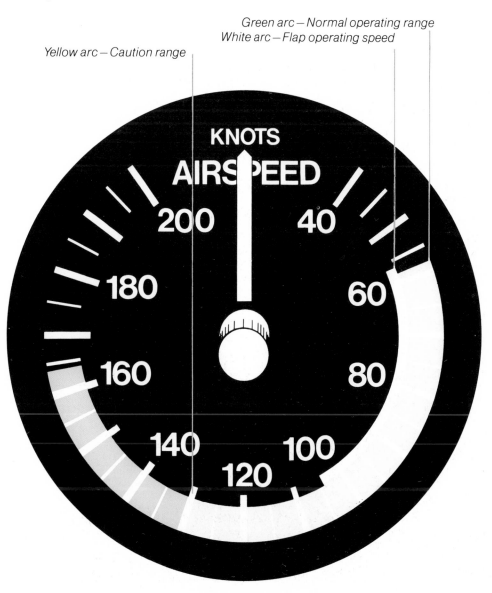

Yellow arc — Caution range

Green arc — Normal operating range
White arc — Flap operating speed

Slipstream effect

3 As we shall be changing the power we need to be aware of something called 'slipstream effect' and its impact on the bane of some pilots' lives, called 'the Ball'. Briefly, the slipstream made by the propeller does

A force of air hitting the fin and rudder from one side is obviously going to slew the aircraft round, just as though the rudder itself had been stuck out into the airflow. At normal cruising speeds this is taken care of on the Cheetah by a piece of metal fixed to the rudder and angled slightly to the left.

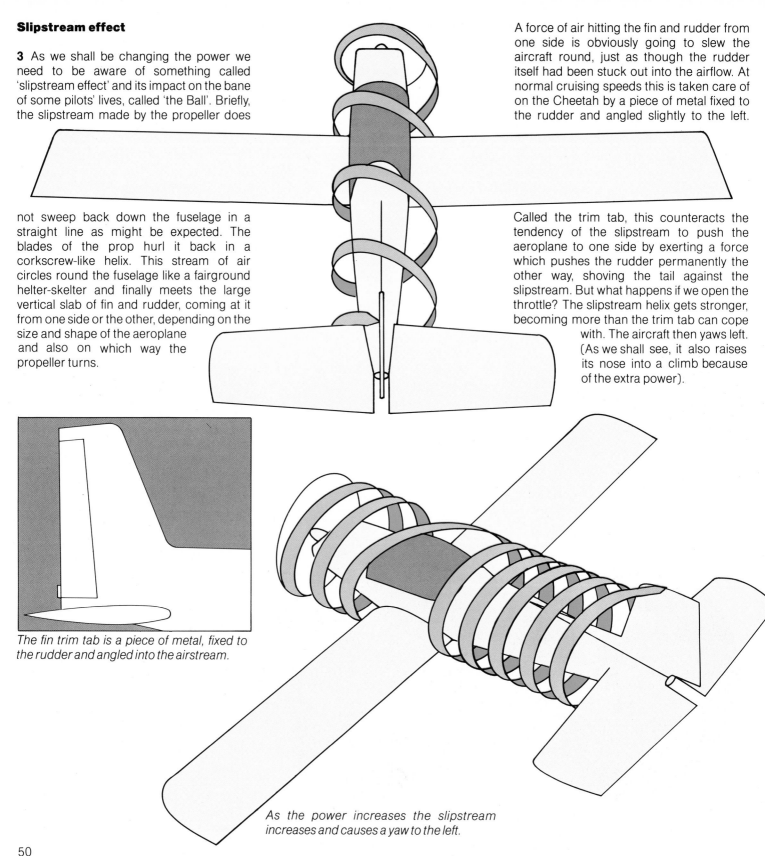

not sweep back down the fuselage in a straight line as might be expected. The blades of the prop hurl it back in a corkscrew-like helix. This stream of air circles round the fuselage like a fairground helter-skelter and finally meets the large vertical slab of fin and rudder, coming at it from one side or the other, depending on the size and shape of the aeroplane and also on which way the propeller turns.

Called the trim tab, this counteracts the tendency of the slipstream to push the aeroplane to one side by exerting a force which pushes the rudder permanently the other way, shoving the tail against the slipstream. But what happens if we open the throttle? The slipstream helix gets stronger, becoming more than the trim tab can cope with. The aircraft then yaws left. (As we shall see, it also raises its nose into a climb because of the extra power).

The fin trim tab is a piece of metal, fixed to the rudder and angled into the airstream.

As the power increases the slipstream increases and causes a yaw to the left.

In order to keep our flying tidy we need to help the trim tab out and counteract that yaw with a touch of right rudder. Where does the Ball come into all this? It is the small, spirit level-like black ball at the bottom of the turn-and-slip indicator. Only when that ball is in the middle between the two black hair-lines is the aircraft flying in a properly balanced way. If the aeroplane is slipping or skidding in any direction, the ball will shoot to that side of the small, curved tube. Opening the throttle on the Cheetah will, as explained, punch the nose over to the left, causing a skid to the right. The ball will register it. (So, as I later found to my pain, will the eyes of the test examiner). A touch of right rudder (in the Cheetah's case) is what is needed. The rule for reacting to the ball is beautifully simple. Whichever side it goes to, that is the side on which you need to put pressure on the rudder pedal in order to get back into balance. It is called 'treading the ball'. Conversely, when power is taken off, the pounding on the side of the fin and rudder will ease off and the rudder pressure will no longer be needed. There may even be the need for a dab of rudder the other way. The ball will tell. In time it should become an automatic gesture with the feet every time the throttle is moved.

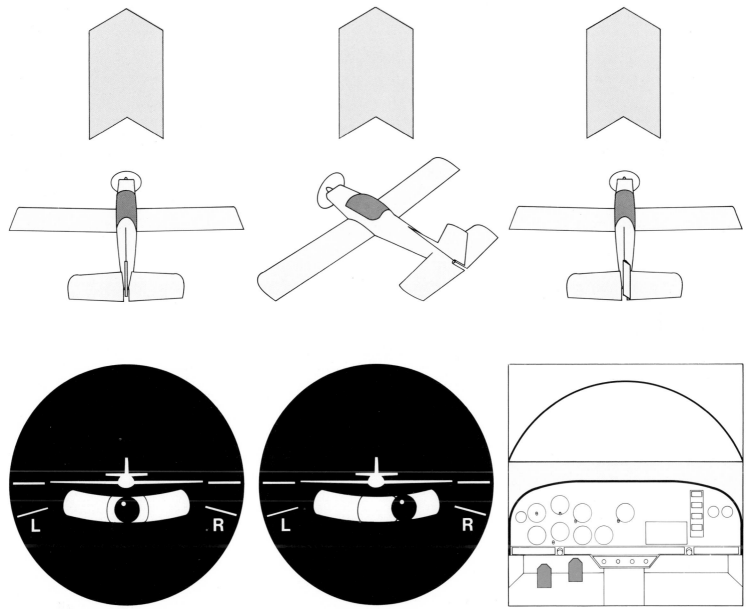

When flying straight the ball will be in the centre of the turn-and-slip indicator.

When the throttle is opened, the aircraft yaws, and the ball moves in the direction of slip.

To counteract the yaw produced by increased power, put on a touch of right rudder.

The use of power

Now to the day's work itself.

As a start we were going to look at the effects of changing the power. I was to bring the revs back to 1500 RPM, see how the nose dropped and edged over to the right. Then increase to full power and see how the opposite happened. Having taken note of the feel of that I was going to try to stop the nose going up or down by using the elevators, and correcting the yaw to right and left by using the rudder. Jeanne had an oft-repeated phrase to describe this process, one of the cliches of flying instruction: 'I want you to maintain that nose attitude'. Maintaining the nose attitude infers having a settled idea of what the picture looks like out of the windscreen in the first place. Where does the nose come in relation to the horizon in normal level flight at a certain power setting? It varies with different types of aeroplane, just as in some motor cars you can see a long bonnet stretching in front of you and in some cars you can't see any bonnet at all. The AA5A Cheetah cruises level in a comparatively nose down way, with the nose quite appreciably below the horizon. We shall need to burn that forward picture into our mind's eye. It's the key to the whole business.

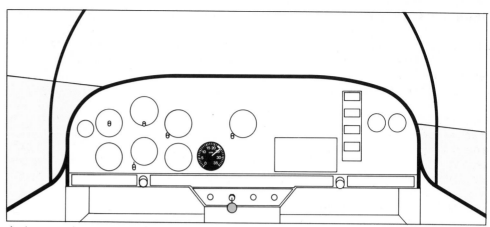

An increase in power lifts the nose to the left

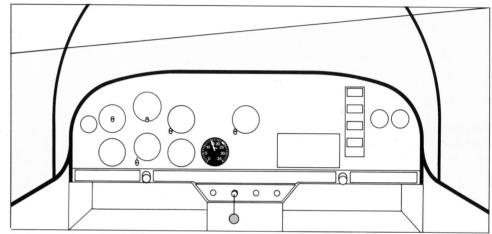

A decrease in power will lower the nose and cause a yaw to the right

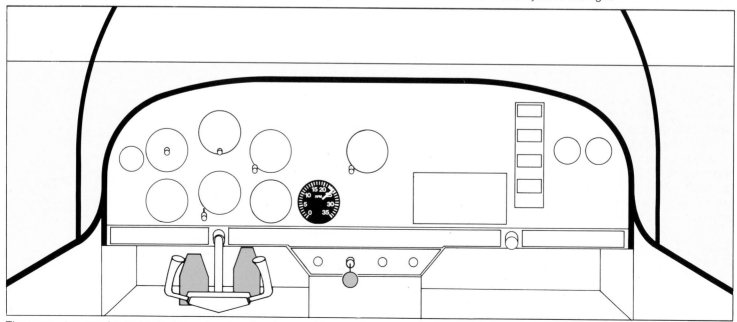

The nose rise can be corrected by using the elevators and the yaw is corrected by a touch of right rudder

The use of the flaps

Then we would be seeing what the flaps will do. But first I was instructed in the correct technique for carrying out this supposedly simple operation of using the flap switch.

I was to put the flaps down and count how many seconds it took for them to go fully extended. (My own method of counting seconds is to go 'One-di-dah, Two-di-dah etc', but there is, I know, a school of thought which believes in the 'One thousand, Two thousand, Three thousand' method. I suppose people choose whichever makes them feel least ridiculous). I was then to bring them up and count how long it took for them to make the return journey. The result of this exercise would show that they come up a lot faster than they go down (because the airflow is helping to push them), and that their downward trip takes around nine seconds on this aircraft.

But there are four stages of flap: fully up, one third, two thirds and fully down. From which we can calculate that it will take three seconds to put a third down, or six seconds to put two thirds down. This is worth knowing, because it allows us to select whatever flap setting we want without having to peer down between the seats at the indicator by the switch. It will allow us to keep looking out instead of having our noses stuck in the cockpit. 'That's vital', said Jeanne. 'I can't impress that on you enough'. I discovered later just what a useful technique this is. The most common moment for putting some flap on is when approaching the airfield to make a landing, a time when I found myself not only looking out for all the other aircraft around but concentrating grimly on the runway and flight instruments to make sure that I was judging the approach correctly. All I had to do was feel for the switch and mouth 'One-di-dah, Two-di-dah, Three-di-dah', and there was a third of flap.

But what do the flaps actually do? And how do they do it?

There are various types, but on the AA5A they are the most basic of all, sections of the trailing edge of the inner part of the wing which simply fold down.

They increase the camber of the wing, therefore generating more lift. To hark back to our basic aerodynamics, the airflow underneath the wing will have a bit extra to push up against. On the top surface the extra bit of curve the air will have to travel over will reduce the pressure still more, and contribute its portion to the extra lift. But, of course, nothing is free. The cost of sticking flaps down into the airstream is paid for in extra drag. (Drag is explained later). The cost varies, depending on how much flap is used.

The effects of flaps

The first third produces the greatest benefit; you get a little bit of drag but quite a lot of lift. The second third gives scarcely more lift but a lot more drag. Full flap is mostly drag, acting like an airbrake, and is used for the approach when coming in to land, except in a crosswind.

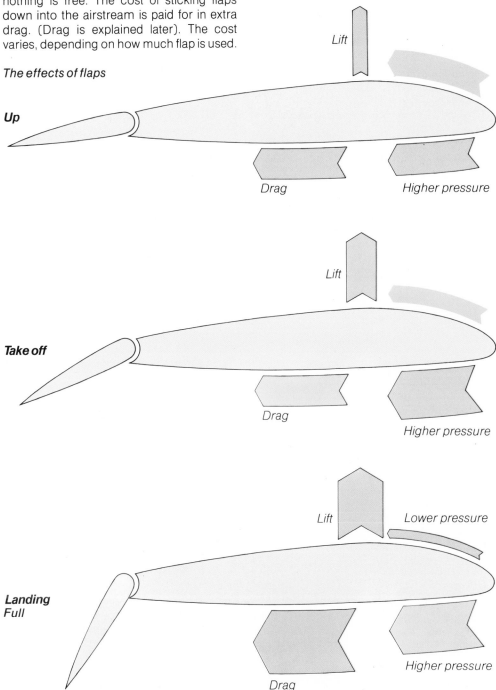

Up

Lift

Drag   Higher pressure

Take off

Lift

Drag

Higher pressure

Landing Full

Lift   Lower pressure

Drag   Higher pressure

Flap exercise

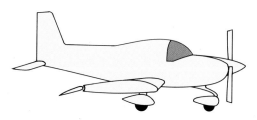

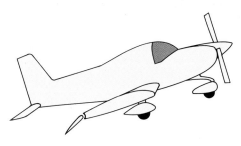

As the first third of flap is lowered the aircraft pitches up. To counteract this feed in some forward pressure on the stick.

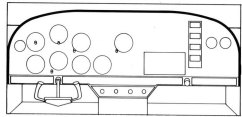

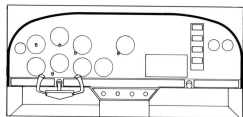

On this exercise we are not only going to see what the flaps do, but also learn how to control that effect. The first third of the flap is the liveliest. The Cheetah pitches up quite quickly although most aircraft designs tend to pitch down when flap is applied. But it all depends on the type of aircraft. To stop it

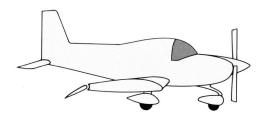

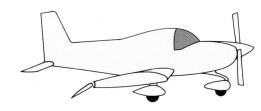

The second third of flap down requires far less of a counter measure.

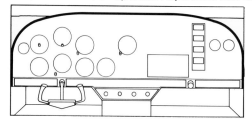

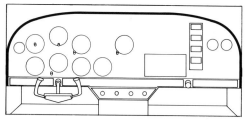

happening and carry on with a smooth level flight requires the pilot to be ready for it. The trick is to catch it by feeding in some forward pressure on the control column before the plane had had time to oscillate, so that the passenger couldn't even tell that some flap had come down. Judging it just right is a very satisfactory experience, and comes under

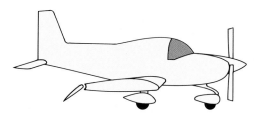

Full flap will need a backward pull as the drag tends to make the aircraft sink slightly.

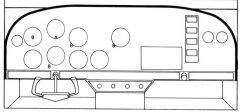

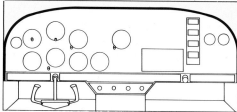

the heading of 'getting to know your aeroplane'. Putting on the second third requires far less of a counter measure, just a slight nudge forward of the control column should be enough. To stay level while selecting the final full flap stage will even mean bringing the stick back a bit, as the colossal drag tends to overwhelm the lift.

54

Raising the flaps causes the aircraft I learned on, the Cheetah, to sink slightly.

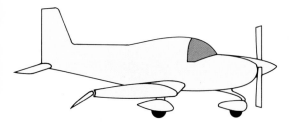

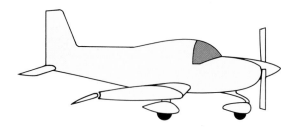

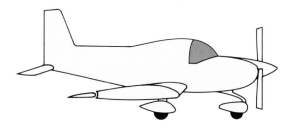

Flap off exercise

Raising the flaps (people rarely seem to talk about 'putting them up') has the reverse effect, requiring the opposite counter measures. Once again, the one to watch is that first stage of flap (although, of course, it will be the stage we come to last when raising flaps). Instead of rising this time, she sinks as that final bit goes up. Incidentally we do not raise the flaps in one continuous motion. They go up in stages, allowing the

aircraft to digest each new situation before going on to the next. This is a vital habit to get into for the reason that one of the commonest occasions on which a pilot needs to remove all the flap is when he/she has abandoned a landing for some reason and is climbing away again in an overshoot. With full flap the airspeed will not be very high, even at full throttle. Taking all the flap up at once is going to bring about a sink which could be quite nasty if the aircraft was close to the ground. So they are brought up in

stages, allowing the aircraft to pick up its enthusiasm for flying between stages (which will come from having had some of the drag removed). Mastering the smooth removal of the touchy first third is important, because it is something we shall have to do practically every time we take off. We shall come to that when covering the take off, but it is worth bearing in mind that retracting the third of flap used for getting off the runway without a sink is something our passengers will be grateful for.

Trim tabs: these help take the effort out of moving the control surfaces. By extending out into the airstream (right) they serve to push the elevator up, and correctly set for a given airspeed, allow the aircraft to be flown 'hands off'.

Trim tabs

There is one more skill we shall be introduced to on this trip: the use of the trimmer. We have already discovered the trim tabs on the back of the elevators. They are a boon to neat unflustered flying. How they work is shown in the illustration.

It would be very tedious if pilots had to compensate for every change of power or use of flap by pushing or pulling the control column and holding it, against a force, in its new position. The trimmer, worked by its small wheel between the seats, holds the elevators where we want them. If, for example, we want to climb at a certain speed, we bring the stick back and wait until she steadies herself down at that speed. We shall need to exert a constant backwards pressure on the column to keep it in place. By putting our right hand down to the trim wheel and swivelling it back a bit we shall feel

gradually less pull is needed to keep the control column in position. Eventually, with just the right amount of backward turn on the trim wheel, the control column will stay in its backward position of its own accord; or, as they say, trimmed.

If you are having to push the column forward, you trim by moving the trim wheel forward. Pulling back means trimming back. You know you have trimmed properly when you can take your hand off the control column and find that it stays put.

There are some bad habits attached to trimming. One is to use the trim wheel to adjust the attitude of the aeroplane, instead of using the control column, and then following up with with the trim. Another is to trim too early, before the aircraft has settled down properly; so that you may have to trim again, and again ... All of which means that the aircraft may wander before reaching the right height.

People who know their aircraft *do* cheat. They will know, for instance, that in order to get their beloved flying machine into a steady glide from a straight and level cruise they only need to take off the power and give three and a bit twirls on the trim wheel, and she will look after herself while they get on with something else. Saving time and effort with that kind of dodge is one of the rewards of experience.

When we took off to try these things it turned out to be one of those bumpy days when it is hard enough to keep the aircraft steady without having to contend with changes of power and flap as well. I discovered that in bumpy weather it is pointless to grip the control column and try to counteract every lurch and roll with a move in the opposite direction. Provided she was properly trimmed, she seemed better able to look after herself, with only an occasional gentle nudge to bring the wings level.

control column to keep the nose in place at first. But aeroplanes (our kind, at least) do not accelerate suddenly.

The speed builds up gradually, increasing lift proportionately. I discovered therefore that the force needed to keep the nose in place also gradually increased. The control

'Getting the picture', or 'getting the nose right', as Jeanne called it, is something that every pilot has to work out for themselves. The view out front at 100 knots cruising speed will depend on whether it is a tall pilot with his head brushing the cabin top or a small pilot with no cushion peering over the instrument panel. It isn't something that you can be told. It has to be seen. The process of changing the attitude, and altering power and flaps, helped me to identify what the normal attitude should be. As Jeanne went through each manoeuvre and its correction I followed her through, with my hands lightly on the controls. Then it was my turn. One key element of wisdom began to dawn. The control column is very sensitive. What it does to an aircraft depends very much on how fast the air is moving past the control surfaces and the wings at the time. When I put on full power, for instance, it needed only a moderately light forward pressure of the

column is not like a switch, that is moved unfeelingly to get a desired effect. It has to be nursed all the time. At first I found that the altimeter showed that I would start off by keeping level after the increase of power, but that eventually I would begin creeping upwards. I wasn't compensating for the build up of speed. Neat accurate flying began to seem an unexpectedly delicate process needing much concentration.

NO HOLD

57

Chapter 6: Straight and level: the instruments

Straight and level I

To fly 'straight and level' doesn't sound all that demanding, but it looks a bit harder when the instruction is: 'to fly the aircraft at 100 knots in a constant direction, at a constant altitude and in balance'. These are a lot of things to consider at once. 'You will be learning to do something calculated to the aeroplane', said Jeanne, 'rather than discovering what it does to you'.

The importance of flying in a straight line along a chosen course when flying across country from A to B is obvious. It has to be done at a pre-selected altitude to clear obstacles and keep air traffic controllers happy. It has to be at your pre-selected speed, because you will have made important predictions about when you are going to arrive at each point and how much fuel you are going to need on the way. So direction, height and speed are vital. The aeroplane needs to be in balance (about which more will be said shortly) because it doesn't fly comfortably or efficiently unless it is.

In order to do all this I was compelled to make closer acquaintance with instruments which I had been observing fairly distantly and spasmodically up to now. To take them in order:

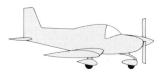

1 The Airspeed Indicator (ASI)
Previously we have noticed our speeds at various flap and power settings. We have also watched the needle come back as we lost speed in order to put on flap. Now comes the task of bringing the needle to a selected cruising speed and keeping it there. (It's a nice, round 100 knots in the AA5A Cheetah's case).

2 The Altimeter
No need to know how it works at this stage, or about the niceties of altimeter settings (about which all was revealed when we came to climbing and descending). What we shall have to do is keep snatching a look at the needle of the instrument to note whether we are edging up or down. If we are, we shall have to do something about it, or our 'constant altitude' will go to pot.

3 The Vertical Speed Indicator (VSI)
It shows how fast we are climbing or descending. Obviously, it should not show any rise or fall.

4 Direction Indicator (DI) and Magnetic Compass
I have met pilots who are not happy unless they are finding their way about the landscape with the use of nothing but a weighty, old-fashioned compass which fills up most of the lower part of their cockpits and demands the constant adjustment of hairlines coupled with intense mental arithmetic. Life is now easier, though the magnetic compass, even the small one to be found at the top of the AA5A's windscreen, remains the basis of our direction finding. But for immediate reference, and for the purpose of keeping 'constant direction', we shall be using the Direction Indicator. It has no north-seeking magnetic properties and is simply a gyro propelled by the aircraft's vacuum system (which we met during the pre-take off checks). Gyros have the habit, as all who have played with one will know, of 'maintaining a constant orientation in space irrespective of the movement of the surrounding structure', as the dictionary has it. It stays put as long as it keeps spinning. So if it is lined up with the compass on magnetic north it will behave almost as though it were a magnetic compass itself, and be a lot less

jerky, temperamental and easy to read in the process. The catch lies in that 'almost'. The rotation of the earth moves us, plus magnetic north, around 15 degrees an hour. But the DI continues to point at the spot in space it was set to—doggedly 'maintaining a constant orientation'. So we need to reset it every fifteen or twenty minutes. (The odd one or two degrees don't matter, because we won't be able to fly that accurately anyway). In order to reset it we have to make sure that the compass is absolutely steady and not bobbing around because we are turning, or because of turbulence. Wait for a calm moment when she is just sitting there. On a long cross country it is common for students

that we can cut down on the fuel part of the mixture. Fully in is as rich as you need at ground level. Fully out is the other end of the spectrum, and will be so 'lean' that it will cut off the fuel and stop the engine. Somewhere in between is the right position for cruising at any altitude within the capabilities of the aeroplane, the minimum amount of fuel for the air available. Properly handled you can find yourself saving about 15 per cent of fuel. How is it done? Having settled down in straight and level flight we need to look at the RPM gauge as we gently ease out the mixture control knob. If we yank it out with a great heave the engine will start coughing and we shall have to start again. But if we pull

Each mixture setting serves only for that power setting. So don't do it if you are about to play about with the power, and always shove it back in to rich before you do change the power. Also, never have a leaned off mixture on full power. Engine splutter would result. (5000 feet and above is when you can really feel and hear the benefit).

A moment's thought will show that there is only one power setting (or spot on the Rev Counter) which will give 100 knots in level flight. Too much power, she'll rise or go faster. Too little, she'll sink or go more slowly, depending on what the pilot is doing with the control column or the way the aircraft is

4

5

6

to forget about re-setting the DI because of all the other anxieties and problems, which means that it could become 15 degrees out after an hour, giving them more problems.

5 The Artificial Horizon

This is the instrument, discussed in Chapter 10, showing the position of the aircraft relative to the horizon, and how far it is banking.

6 The Rev Counter (RPM gauge).

This was also to be the time when I made closer acquaintance with the mixture control (red knob beside throttle), and the process known as 'leaning off'. At higher altitudes, where the atmosphere is thinner, there is not enough air to burn all the petrol injected into the cylinder. The mixture control is there so

it out little by little we will find that the RPM gauge will first of all pick up a little bit and then drop. When it drops we know that we must be very slightly starving the engine, so the position must be somewhere about there. The time between the pick up and the drop is small, so it is the drop we shall notice most. When we get that we simply return the control a quarter of an inch and leave it there. We are going to end up with a slightly rich mixture, but that is no bad thing. Extra fuel going into the cylinders acts as a cooling agent. Take that away and run the engine on an over-lean mixture and the result will be over-heating and all sorts of diabolical problems. Another point: there is no use in leaning the mixture if you are about to change the power setting to climb or descend.

trimmed. How do we know what power to use? Trial and error. It varies from aircraft to aircraft, even of the same type, depending on whether it is covered with mud, how heavy the passengers are, how much fuel is on board, how old the aircraft is and so on. In the Cheetah it is normally between 2200 to 2300 RPM. As a start we usually stick the power on 2200 RPM, where the green arc on the RPM gauge begins (signifying Normal Operating Range). If that doesn't seem to be doing the job we can nudge the throttle in a bit and re-trim. You can have no idea of the feeling of triumph and satisfaction which comes from getting the aircraft purring along with the Altimeter needle slap on 2000 (say) and staying there, and the ASI slap on 100, and staying there.

It is quite true that, as the old hands will undoubtedly remark, too much time can be spent concentrating on the instruments and fiddling with gadgets. In the old days people learned to fly straight and level by the look of the horizon, the sound of the engine note or the hum of the bracing wires. But nowadays pilots are a bit more enclosed, removed from the elements. The right 'feel' will undoubtedly come in time. But the instruments (as long as they are working properly) are the way to get it right at the beginning.

But how?

We started by looking at the straight element of straight and level. To begin with Jeanne asked what seemed like an easy question: 'When I ask you to fly towards a certain

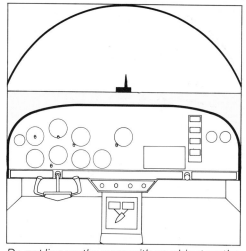

Do not line up the nose with an object on the horizon...

object or structure, what part of the aeroplane do you point at it?'

'The nose?'

'Everyone says that. It's wrong.'

It wouldn't be wrong if we were sitting directly behind the nose, in a single-seater or an aircraft with tandem seating, like the Chipmunk. But in the Cheetah, with side-by-side seating, the pilot is not sitting behind the nose, he is sitting to one side of it. Although the two seats are only about eighteen inches apart, what the two occupants see by looking straight over the nose will be quite different from each other.

Therefore, if the pilot points the nose at something he will be aiming at an object to one side, and will proceed in a curve, not a straight line.

... for your position left of the centre line will cause you to fly in a curve

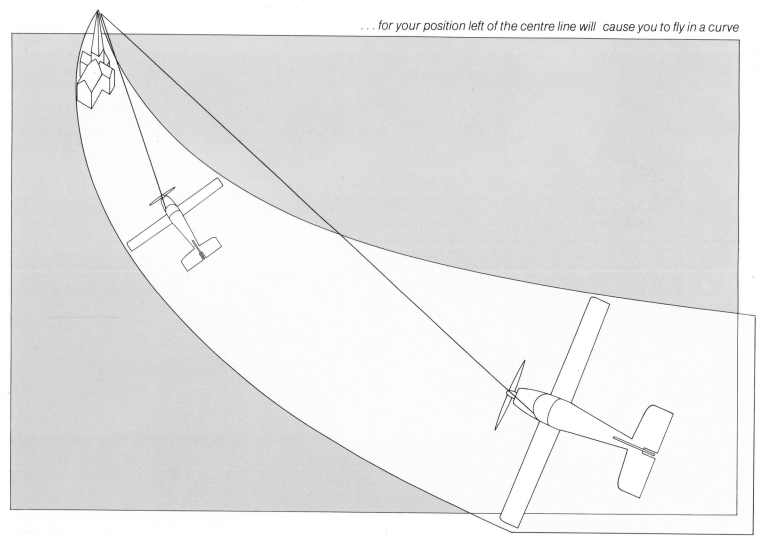

The answer is to look straight ahead, through the middle of the control column at its neutral position in front of us, and line any target or landmark up on that. As it happens the Cheetah makes life even easier, because on top of the instrument panel, in front of each seat, is a small air vent which sticks up into the line of vision like a sight. All we have to do is steer straight towards a landmark is place it in line with our ventilator.

We may be steering a heading on the Direction Indicator. But there is no harm in picking out a landmark that corresponds with that heading and steering by that, keeping a good lookout as well.

Wandering off target can be corrected with a bit of bank, bringing the whole aircraft round. Correcting with the rudder alone simply

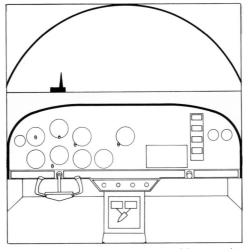

The correct way to line up an object on the horizon . . .

produces yaw and a sideways slide, with the aircraft zipping back into its original position with hardly any change of heading having taken place, as soon as the rudder is taken off. Strictly speaking, a touch of rudder should go with the bank, but for slight corrections the Cheetah seems to respond to the ailerons alone and make a gentle course alteration without losing any balance or upsetting the ball.

We should also watch that we keep the wings level. The ball of the Slip Indicator will reveal any problems there, but we can look outside to see that the top of the engine cowling is parallel to the horizon, with the wings in the same relative position to the horizon each side. While looking round to check this we shall, of course, simultaneously be keeping a good lookout.

. . . taking into account the pilot's position in the aircraft

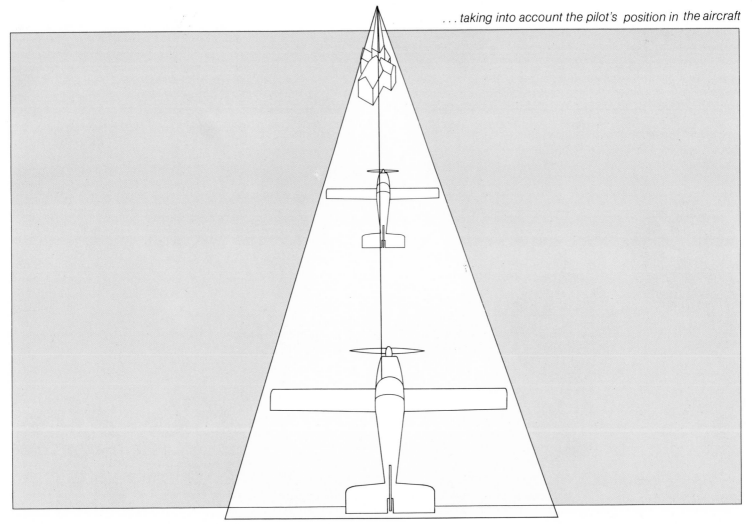

So much for the STRAIGHT. Now what about the LEVEL?

The right power and the right nose attitude are the things which jointly decide whether you are going to keep that Altimeter needle glued to its selected figure. The look of the nose relative to the horizon in a level cruise is something that every pilot has to find for himself. It depends, as we said, on whether the pilot is tall or short. It also depends on the type of aeroplane. But how can we quickly find it out for ourselves? What Jeanne proposed to do was settle the aeroplane in a

level cruise for me so that I could look out forward and burn that picture in my brain. I was then to take over and try to keep her steady. If we started to edge up it would mean that I was holding the nose too high. If we started to sink, it was too low. By this trial and error method I was to grasp that all-important concept: 'the Correct Nose Attitude, as it is called.

But there was a word of warning about the correct way to respond to what the Altimeter or for that matter the Airspeed Indicator are saying: 'Never chase the instruments'. The fault most beginners make is to over-react, with too many hurried adjustments and counter-adjustments. I would find, for instance, that the Altimeter needle had climbed to 2100 feet, instead of 2000 feet. So I would put the nose down and watch the needle stop climbing and start descending back to 2000 feet. As we got to the desired height I would level out again. But to my consternation, the needle would carry on downwards, below 2000 feet, so I would pull the stick back to stop it and start climbing back up again. Back we came, past 2000 feet, and

Wait until the instrument responds before making further corrections

on upwards. So forward with the stick again, so that the aircraft proceeded up, down, up, down, like the dreaded yo-yo. The fact is that the Altimeter does not register instantaneously what is happening. Nor can the aircraft accelerate or decelerate immediately in response to slight adjustments of the controls (although the ASI gives more or less instant speed readings). Therefore it is no use trying to chase the needles. The correct method is to use the instruments to size up the situation, make what you think is an appropriate correction, and then wait and see what happens before making any other adjustment. In time you will come to be able to judge how much correction is needed by noting how fast (for instance) the Altimeter needle is going up or down. So if you have got 90 knots and are climbing and want 100 knots in level flight, just nudge the nose down and see what the needle does. If it edges to 95 and sticks you will know that a bit more adjustment is needed to get it right. But it is much more satisfactory — and time-saving — to make a prediction and see what happens than to chase the needles or (to use another way of describing it) 'hunt the airspeed'.

The important thing to remember is that nose attitude and power are inter-related. If we find ourselves keeping a satisfactory level flight but only clocking up 95 knots it is obviously pointless to lower the nose a fraction to get more speed and leave it at that. We shall only have got our desired speed by sacrificing height. What is needed is a slight nudge of extra power while we lower the nose a little and re-trim the aeroplane at the desired speed.

And what of the final injunction, that the aircraft should be 'in balance' — that is, the machine is neither skidding or slipping and the balance indicator, which is normally a ball, is in the middle. Provided we have a good, clear, level horizon to work on this should not be too much of a problem. But it may be that a bank of cloud or mist is obscuring the horizon, or that a gently sloping cloud bank may be giving us a false, tilted horizon. Flying with the wings lined up to that false horizon would mean that one wing was down, which (as we have learnt) would start the aircraft yawing towards the lower wing. Correcting that yaw with the rudder is going to mean that the aircraft will be flying slightly

sideways, or crab-wise. This, in turn, will mean that more power will be needed to achieve a given speed.

In total the aircraft will be 'out of balance' and generally unhappy. We should probably feel it through our seats, as the weight of the body is thrown slightly towards one side of the aircraft or the other. What is certain is that the ball of the Turn and Slip Indicator will be over towards the downward side. Levelling the wings (and taking off the compensatory rudder pressure) should bring it back to the centre again, between the vertical hairlines on the Slip Indicator. The aeroplane will then be in balance, and happy.

A good horizon is needed to practice this lesson. I quickly came to realise that good horizons are rarer than might be imagined. What seems like a bright sunny day on the ground can in fact be a dense unpleasant day in the air, with a veil of moist mist obscuring the join between land and sky. An apparently 'cloudless sky' can be a sky totally covered with a faint, white haze.

My introduction to straight and level was on a good clear day, but the disadvantage was that it was also a bumpy one. You rarely get everything right. No sooner had I got the aeroplane settled down and trimmed than she would start lurching upwards for no apparent reason, with the Altimeter needle edging round the dial. Why did she do that? A thermal (a bubble of hot air rising up from the ground) had taken us with it. It was just a matter of edging the nose down a fraction until we had got back to our desired height. I quickly realised that the important thing is to get the machine properly settled down to begin with, with the right revs and the right nose attitude. Once you have got that sorted out, any minor corrections of altitude can be made by merely edging the stick forwards or backwards until you get back the height you want. Of course, the speed will change while you are making the correction (increasing or decreasing, depending on whether you are going down or up), but it will soon come back to the chosen 100 knots once you have levelled out at your correct altitude again.

The 'straight' part of the operation was easy enough. The Direction Indicator is a simple instrument to follow, without any of the

delayed action effect which needs such careful handling when attempting to fly neatly and accurately from the Altimeter and, due to aircraft inertia, the Airspeed Indicator. There is also a usefully direct connection between the message given by the DI's dial and the action needed to respond to it. When the needle shows you have drifted five degrees to the left of the required heading, the action of turning the yoke over for a gentle bank to the right seems a logical and natural thing to do. It is difficult to get it wrong, and bank the wrong way (though I did manage it once or twice). Also, the dial registers your change of heading instantly, and stops dead in its tracks as soon as you have levelled out, which makes for a pleasing accuracy.

I was made to fly straight and level towards a visual object, such as a white multi-storey building sticking up from the middle of Potters Bar, or a corner of the Lea Valley reservoir system, while keeping a good look-out for other aircraft at the same time. Having picked one aiming point, I had to get ready with another one on the same heading further on, before the first one disappeared below the nose. While doing this it was necessary to take an occasional scan of the instruments, to check height, speed and also that the Direction Indicator was still agreeing with the compass and giving us the correct course.

I was to get plenty of practice at this. In the weeks ahead every training session involved a bit of straight and level cruising towards the area of sky to the east of the aerodrome which we used for learning new manoeuvres. I also found myself being given the task of flying part of the circuit round the airfield as we were coming in to land, particularly the 'downwind' stretch. It was simple 'straight and level', the 'straight' part being the correct course for the downwind leg of the circuit which runs parallel to the runway (we shall come to that in more detail when we come to circuit flying), and the 'level' needing accurate flying at the 'circuit height' of 1000 feet.

After fifty minutes of this I felt I was 'getting the picture right'. Then it was back down to the ground and into the Briefing Room to learn about keeping straight and level while varying the speed and the power of the aircraft and using flaps.

Chapter 7: Straight and level: not so easy

Keeping the aeroplane at a steady height when she is nicely settled down at a constant cruising speed is one thing. Keeping her straight and level while varying the speed, either by changing the power or by using some flap, is another matter.

We have already seen what happens when we increase power and speed. There is more lift available, which makes the aircraft want to climb. Decreasing the power has the opposite effect. Putting on some flap also adds to the lift. So if we want to keep to the same height with these changes of power and flap we are going to have to do some deft work with the control column to counteract the effects. The main purpose of this exercise, I discovered later, was to teach the smooth, co-ordinated use of the control column and rudder when making changes of power and flap. All the movements should flow into each other so that the Altimeter needle stays steady and the passengers feel nothing but a slight change of engine note and shift of nose attitude. It is an exercise to teach dexterity. The image of the organist came up again, with hands and feet working rhythmically together to control the aircraft.

This was also to be my introduction to three letters which were to dominate my future training: P-A-T, standing for Power, Attitude and Trim. This is the golden formula telling us the order in which we do things every time we change the height or speed of the aeroplane — with one vital exception (which we meet later in Climbing and Descending). I began to see 'Pat' as a slightly pedantic schoolmistress, wagging her fat, stubby finger every time I was about to do something to the aeroplane.

Jeanne began by writing the three letters P, A, T down one side of the blackboard. She then filled in three columns, one for increasing power, one for decreasing power, and one for using flap. In each column she marked the various actions, in their P-A-T order, needed to arrive at straight level flight in each case. Her diagram looked something like the diagram reproduced at the bottom of this page.

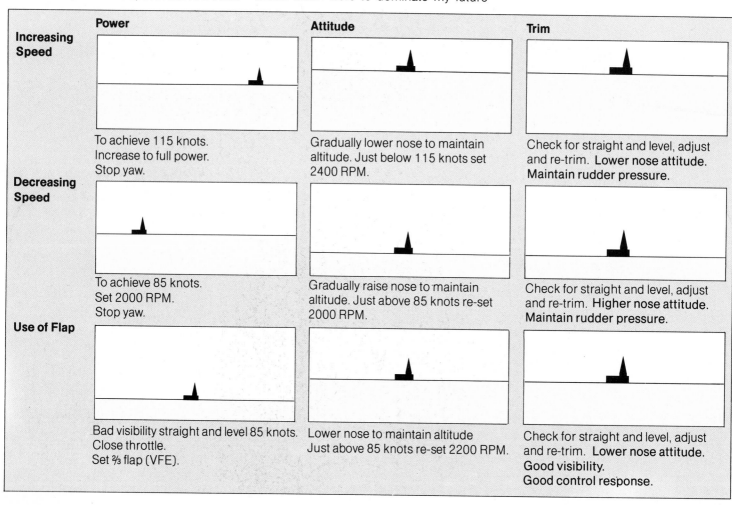

	Power	Attitude	Trim
Increasing Speed	To achieve 115 knots. Increase to full power. Stop yaw.	Gradually lower nose to maintain altitude. Just below 115 knots set 2400 RPM.	Check for straight and level, adjust and re-trim. **Lower nose attitude. Maintain rudder pressure.**
Decreasing Speed	To achieve 85 knots. Set 2000 RPM. Stop yaw.	Gradually raise nose to maintain altitude. Just above 85 knots re-set 2000 RPM.	Check for straight and level, adjust and re-trim. **Higher nose attitude. Maintain rudder pressure.**
Use of Flap	Bad visibility straight and level 85 knots. Close throttle. Set ⅔ flap (VFE).	Lower nose to maintain altitude Just above 85 knots re-set 2200 RPM.	Check for straight and level, adjust and re-trim. **Lower nose attitude. Good visibility. Good control response.**

Increasing Speed

Then we ran through each operation in turn. To step up the speed we push the throttle forward to high power, simultaneously putting on a touch of right rudder pressure to stop the yaw over to the left which will come from the extra slipstream effect. There will be a tendency to climb so we shall need to put on a gradually increasing forward pressure on the wheel. Now, we shall see the speed building up on the Airspeed Indicator. With most piston-engined civil aircraft, first reaction to power is climb. When I came to do it I discovered that it was quite a small amount at first, but by the time the needle was creeping past the 110 mark, the amount of forward push needed to stop the aircraft climbing was quite considerable. As the Airspeed Indicator needle arrives just below the 115 mark it is time to bring back the power to the amount needed to keep it at that speed, which in the Cheetah's case is around 2400 rpm. Of course, the aircraft won't just suddenly stop its acceleration; the momentum will bring her nicely on to the 115 mark, provided you have judged it just right. Then it's time to take the weight of that forward push off the control column by moving the trim wheel forward until she flies along in that attitude by herself. It may be that she will need a bit of adjustment and re-trimming before the Altimeter needle sticks steadily on its chosen spot. To keep her flying straight the slight pressure on the right rudder pedal will probably need to be kept on. The aeroplane is trimmed to fly straight at its cruising speed. At higher speeds she will need some attention from the pilot.

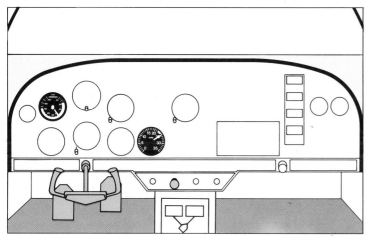

Throttle in to 2500rpm, right rudder, airspeed 100kts

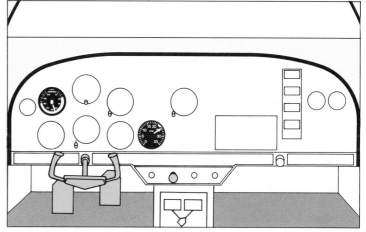

Throttle at 2500rpm, right rudder, airspeed up to 110kts, forward pressure on stick to stop climb

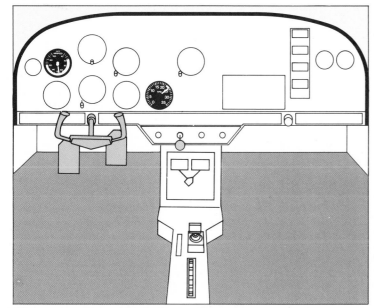

Airspeed 113kts, throttle back slightly to 2400rpm, keep stick forward pressure, right rudder

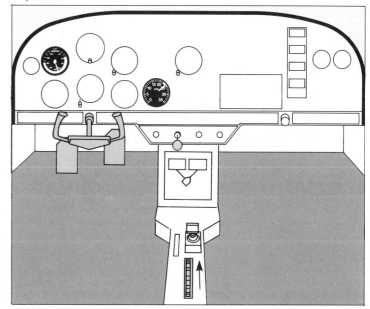

Airspeed steady at 115kts, trim

Decreasing Speed

What about decreasing the speed, and flying slowly? You might need to do this, I was told, if you are coming in to land too close behind another aircraft in the circuit. You could weave or extend your circuit to put a bit more distance between you and the chap in front, or you could slow down, without losing your proper circuit height, of course. Here is how to do it.

Once more, it's P for Power first. This time we bring it back to 2000 revs. There may be some yaw to counteract, coming from the other direction, because we are lessening the side slap of the slipstream vortex, not increasing it. At first the aircraft will want to sink, so we have to raise the nose and in the process, slow down to keep the height. That's A for Attitude. We shall find the speed coming back quite sharply, because we are increasing the angle of attack of the wing and therefore increasing the drag. Just about 85 knots, we take a look at the Rev Counter. We shall see that it has dropped below the 2000 that we started with. This is because as the speed decreases and the nose goes up, so the load on the propeller increases. The engine is having to do progressively more work to keep the aircraft at the same height pulling upwards as well as forwards, with a small amount of 'helicopter effect', and having to overcome a gradually increasing amount of drag as we bring the nose up and add to the angle of attack. So just above 85 knots we give her a small extra bit of throttle to bring the revs back to 2000, fix just the right nose attitude to keep her level at around 85 knots, and trim off the back pressure on the control column. We shan't see a great deal, because the nose will be up somewhere around the horizon. But if we want to go slowly *and* have a good view, then we adopt the third of the three exercises, and use flap.

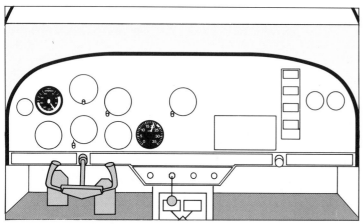

Throttle back to 2000rpm, left rudder, back pressure on stick to stop sink, airspeed drops from 100kts

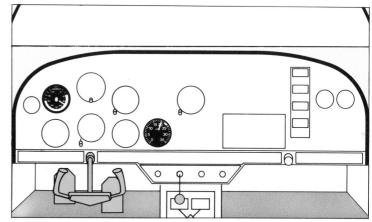

Airspeed 90kts, stick back, left rudder, 2000rpm

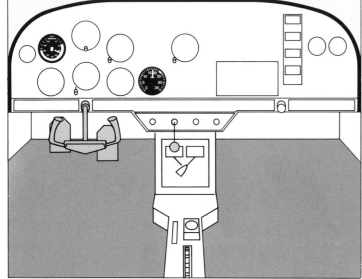

Airspeed 85kts, stick back, left rudder, revs drop to 1900rpm

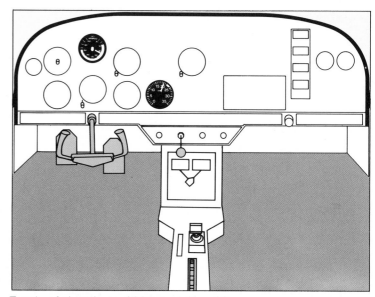

Touch of throttle to 200rpm, left rudder, stick back, airspeed steady at 85kts, trim

Use of flaps

Once more, it is P for Power first. In order to use the flaps we need to get the aeroplane well below the flap limiting speed, so from our straight and level at a 100 Kts we simply close the throttle and keep the nose up to bring the speed back. Then it is on with the flap switch, put down two thirds of flap, simultaneously lowering the nose to counter-act the extra lift and putting the power back on to the 2200 rev cruise power. That's the A for Attitude dealt with. When we have got it just right, so that she is flying level, it is simply T for Trim (which will mean trimming off the forward pressure keeping the nose down in this case). At the end of it all, we shall have an aeroplane flying quite slowly (about 85 knots) because of the drag of the flaps with its nose well down. As we are using normal cruise power there will be a fairly strong draft coming back from the prop, which will make the aircraft feel quite neat and responsive to rudder and elevators, much less sloppy than the nose high, 2000 rev method of getting 85 knots. Above all, we get a good view of what is going on. The low nose presents the best possible picture of the ground ahead. Although, for that reason this is sometimes called 'poor vis straight and level', meaning that it is a useful attitude to take when the visibility is poor and you are creeping along trying to find your way, the most commonly used term is 'Low Safe Cruising Speed'. In such conditions what is needed is a good view and a slow speed, which is what this exercise gives us. You can also see that this 'low·safe cruising speed' attitude is useful when landing.

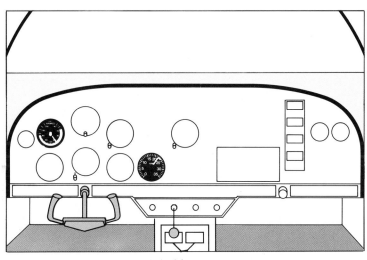

Throttle back, stick back to hold nose up, airspeed dropping

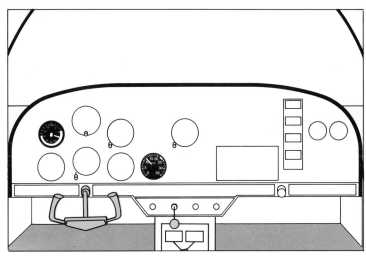

Throttle back, stick back to hold nose up, airspeed dropping

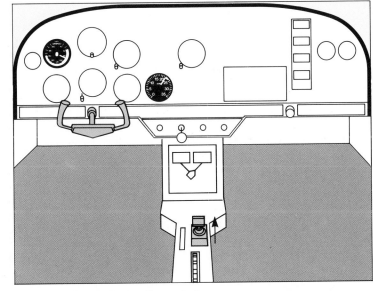

Airspeed 90kts, operate flap switch

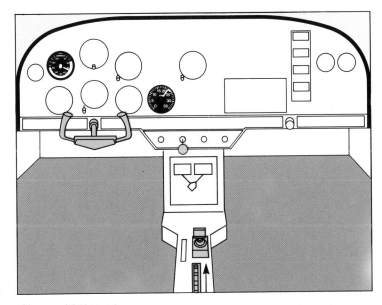

Airspeed 85kts, trim

Speeding up, slowing down exercise

We took off, and after practising the normal straight and level I got the instruction: 'Right, fly me level at 115 knots'. What surprised me was how long it took for the speed to build up. Patience is needed while waiting for the Airspeed Indicator needle to crawl reluctantly round the dial. At first, I left it too late before bringing the power back to 2400, and the speed sailed past to 120 knots. it was interesting to compare the sloppiness of the aircraft at 85 knots and 2000 revs with its taut responsiveness at the higher speed.

Bringing her back to normal cruise straight and level from these various attitudes was just a matter of reversing the various processes, while still sticking to the P-A-T routine. Gradually it became second nature to hold the nose down with my left hand as I pushed the throttle in with my right; and

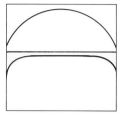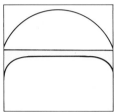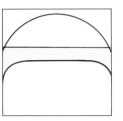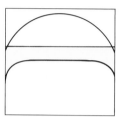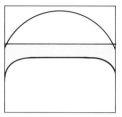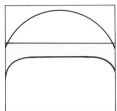

Speeding up exercise

Flying level at 100 knots, 2200rpm

Full throttle, plane starts to climb

Counteract climb by pushing stick forward.

Just below 115kts, bring-back power. Keep forward pressure on

The momentum will bring her on to 115kts

Trim off forward pressure

bring it back as I brought the throttle back. The fact that both hands are moving in the same direction helps. A feeling of smoothness and co-ordination began to come. The trickiest movement of all was getting out of the 'poor vis' attitude back to normal cruise straight and level. The method is to put on high power while holding the nose steady, then take off the flap in two stages, being ready with a backward movement of the stick to counteract the sink as the flaps come up. Then it is back with the power to 2200 as the speed comes up to 100 knots, and trim off any pressure on the control column.

When you can manage all that without allowing the Altimeter needle to deviate more than a few feet from its appointed spot, then you can say you are 'co-ordinated'! And, like many other flying manoeuvres, it gives you an immense amount of satisfaction when you can do it well and smoothly.

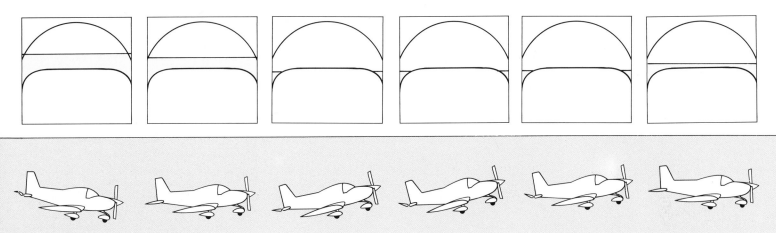

Slowing down exercise

Flying level at 115kts, full throttle out

As power drops nose will want to sink

Pull stick back to maintain altitude

As nose comes up the speed will decrease

As speed comes back to 100kts, feed in cruise power to 2200rpm

Trim for level flight at 100kts

Chapter 8: Going up

Having mastered the problem of keeping the aeroplane flying at one steady height the next move was to learn how to get from one height to another. How, in other words, to get up and down. Also, most importantly, how to level out at the height we want. Experience so far told me that there was going to be a lot more to this than just pulling the nose up or pushing it down and letting her find her own level. How right I was.

But first there were some technicalities and points of airmanship to discuss.

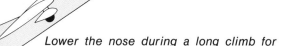

Lower the nose during a long climb for good lookout

1 Looking out in the climb is vital

Other pilots are probably not going to be able to see you climbing underneath them, so we should be careful to look up and behind to make sure that we are not climbing into someone's path.

Apart from that, our nose-high climbing attitude means that we cannot see what is happening immediately in front of us. An aircraft could be flying towards us on a collision course without ever appearing in our line of sight. To avoid that we are advised to lower the nose every now and then during a long climb, just to see what is happening ahead. Some say it should be done every 500 feet, others say every 1000. It obviously depends on visibility. (Others say you can weave from side to side occasionally, but I found that a clumsier way of doing it.)

2 Engine gauges

Climbing requires full power. A long climb involves prolonged maximum strain on the engine, a time when any incipient problems will make themselves known. So we need to keep an eye on the temperature and pressure gauges over on the right. If the oil temperature increases, that is normal; if it nudges the red mark or the oil pressure falls it is time to stop the climb. Something is wrong. As time went on I found myself developing a sixth sense about where the Rev Counter needle ought to be for any given attitude and throttle position. The beginning of some minor trouble, like a faulty plug, will show up there. To spare the engines of the school's Cheetahs the rules decree that we should stay well away from the red line on the Rev Counter, at no more than 2500, so that is something else to watch.

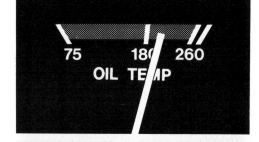

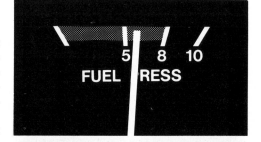

The engine gauges should show roughly these readings during a long climb

3 Altimeter settings

In the pre-flight checks we have already touched on the difference between setting the Altimeter to the height above the ground or the altitude above sea level. For the climbing exercise we have got to know exactly what the Altimeter is telling us, because the London Terminal Control Area, the preserve of the jets coming into Heathrow, begins at 2500 above Elstree. To avoid getting mixed up with them, we don't go above 2400 feet, so it is important to set the Altimeter correctly in order to obey the law and know at exactly what height we are flying. The instrument works by atmospheric pressure, but pressures vary from day to day and from place to place. So we have to be sure that we have the right one for the area and the conditions in which we are flying.

All becomes clear in the great Altimeter setting mystery when we grasp the difference between two sets of three letter codes which get continuously flung around the air waves. They are: (a) the QNH, (b) the QFE. THe QNH is the atmospheric pressure which we set on the Altimeter if we want it to show us our altitude above sea level. The QFE is the pressure which is set on the instrument to show us our height above the airfield for which that particular pressure applies. It is usually given by the control tower.

Personally, I could never remember which was which until someone suggested that QNH stands for Q-Nautical Height and QFE for Q-Field Elevation. Someone else told me they remember it by thinking that QFE is From the Earth. These pressures are given to us by air traffic control in millibars. We set the pressure we want (more about which one to choose when we come to flying round the circuit) by twiddling the setting knob at the bottom of the instrument, peering at the window on the side of the dial until the correct pressure figure comes next to the black marker. (For elderly folk whose eyesight is not what it was, this can be an excruciating business, particularly if I am wearing my wrong glasses at the time. Never mind. Senior airline captains have the same problem and swear by half-frames or bi-focals). Since height is one of the most essential pieces of information for a pilot, it pays to check we have the right setting!

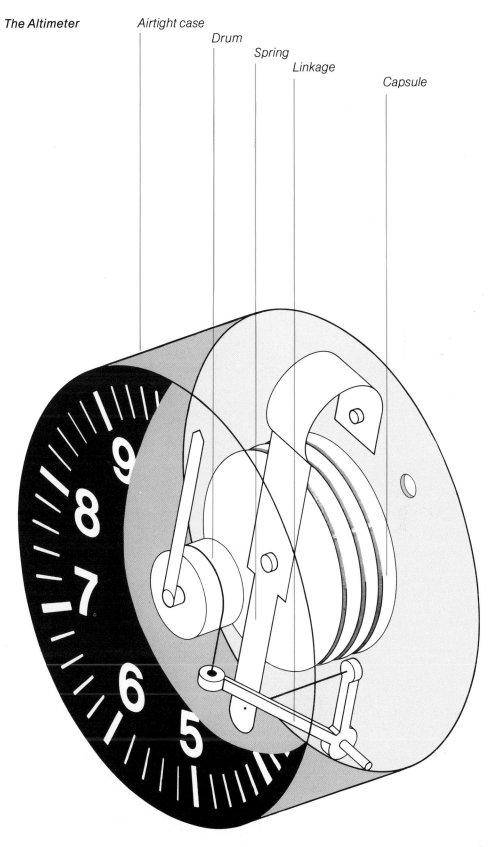

The Altimeter Airtight case Drum Spring Linkage Capsule

It so happens that a rise of thirty feet equals a drop of one millibar in atmospheric pressure. So if we are sitting on an airfield the altitude of which we know to be, for example, 330 feet, then it doesn't take much maths to work out that the difference between the QNH and the QFE for that airfield ought to be 11 mbs. Right? If on this airfield we set the Altimeter to the QNH, an accurate instrument will show roughly 330 feet. (If we put it on the QFE (11 mbs less) it ought to show zero feet).

Above an altitude, which unfortunately varies from one part of the airways system to the next (but is 3000 feet outside controlled airspace) a different system is used. Up there everyone sets their Altimeters to something called the ISA, or International Standard Atmosphere, which is 1013.2 mbs. (We can forget about the .2 because our Altimeter is set to the nearest millibar). They also no longer talk about their altitude (above sea level) or their height (above an airfield) but about their Flight Level, which is a shorthand way of referring to the altitudes shown by Altimeters set to 1013 mbs. It obviously makes sense that everybody's instrument is telling more or less the same story and that one person's 4000 feet is not another person's 4500 feet. Flight levels go up in 500 feet stages and are expressed by knocking the two noughts off the end of the figure. Thus, Flight Level (or FL) Four Zero is 4000 feet on a setting of 1013. (4500 feet would be FL Four Five). So when we hear Concorde's skipper saying he is 'passing through four five zero' we know that somewhere up there in space he is climbing—or descending—through 45000 feet.

We have to remember that none of this tells us the height we are above the ground over which we are flying (apart, of course, from the airfield from which we obtained the QFE). To know our height above the ground we have to know the height of the particular bit of ground we are over. That melancholy fact has caused a lot of grief over the years and is something we are going to have to bear constantly in mind.

A diagram may help make all this a bit clearer than mere words:

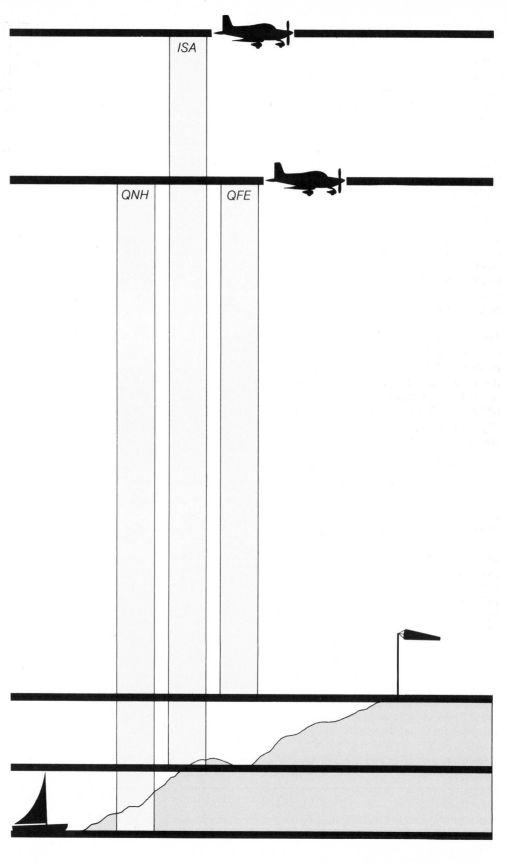

Altitude

4 Quadrantal Rule

This was also the stage when I was introduced to the gigantic, invisible one way traffic system which operates in the skies. The idea is to avoid having aircraft converging on each other at the same height. So everyone flying roughly the same direction has a set of Flight Levels for their use, while people flying in opposite directions have a different set of Flight Levels. The result (provided everyone's Altimeter is accurate and on the common 1032 setting) is that converging aeroplanes should pass 500 feet at least and possibly 1000 feet above or below each other. The diagram below shows how this ingenious rule of the road works. It only applies outside the airways system where pilots do not enjoy the protection of very positive ground control.

Thus, when flying on a Magnetic Track (a path across the ground measured in terms of Magnetic north, which is not necessarily the same as a heading) of between due north (0 degrees) and just short of east (89 degrees) we choose an odd-numbered Flight Level, say FL50, or 5000 feet. Flying between due east and just short of south at 179 degrees an aircraft should be at an odd number PLUS 500 feet. So as we dawdle due north the nearest an aircraft crossing our path at right angles going due east should be is 500 feet above us (which looks close enough when you are up there). As will be seen from the diagram, the really nasty ones, the times when aircraft are coming from diametrically the opposite direction, closing in at the sum of your two speeds (which could very easily be 300 miles per hour or more), should involve a separation of 1000 feet, provided both pilots have remembered how the quadrantal rule works. (You can remember that it is the ODD ones that come first round the clock, because Flight Levels begin with an ODD one, FL30, 3000 feet). The third quarter of the compass, from south to 269 degrees, is flown at even thousands of feet and the final quarter at evens plus 500 feet. Of course none of this obviates the need to keep a good look-out at all times. There is a margin for error on the fringes of the quadrants, and it is also possible to converge on another aircraft going in more or less the same direction. There will also always be the idiot who has got it wrong.

The quadrantal rule

0-89°
Odd thousands of feet

270–359°
Even thousands of feet plus five hundred feet

180–269°
Even thousands of feet

90–179°
Odd thousands of feet plus five hundred feet

During our flying training it is unlikely that we shall be applying these rules, because we don't normally travel anywhere that high up. But one near certainty is that a question involving the quadrantal rule will come in the written exams.

5 The Vertical Speed Indicator

As was mentioned in Chapter six, its function is to reveal just how fast, in hundreds of feet per minute, we are going up or down. During straight and level flying I grew to hate this instrument for the tell-tale way in which it insisted on showing ups and downs when all I wanted was levels. In climbing and descending it became a friend.

Vertical Speed Indicator

73

Some people take climbing and descending as quite separate lessons. We took them together because, as Jeanne put it, 'if you go up you have got to come down'.

Our friend PAT rules again in going into the climb. The object was a good steady balanced climb at 85 knots. So having had a good look where we are going it is P for full power (watch out for that yaw . . .). The nose will begin to strain up of its own accord and we give it some encouragement with the control column until the aircraft is in the particular nose attitude which we know from experience will give us 85 knots. Once more it is a matter of finding out for ourselves what this particular picture looks like. For me it turned out to be when the cowling top was just below the level of the horizon. I started off with it too high and the speed dropped back to 75 knots. A slight forward nudge on the

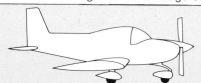

control column and the speed rose up towards the required figure. Once more I was warned about not chasing the Airspeed Indicator. Choose an attitude and then wait and see what that does to the speed. Only when it has settled down should you make an adjustment and then wait and see how that turns out before making another one, if it is required. (What we are doing here, of course, is discovering one of the vital secrets of flying, which is that Speed Is Controlled By The Elevators). Having got the correct speed (which is A for Attitude) we Trim and let her carry on by herself. But do not touch that trim wheel, I was warned, until you are satisfied with what you have got.

There are things to watch during the climb, in addition to keeping a look out above and lowering the nose occasionally to see if anything is happening ahead. I was taught to intersperse the looking out with a systematic glance at one set of instruments at a time. For instance: Look out—then back inside to see if the Airspeed Indicator still shows 85 knots—look out—back to see what kind of a reading is coming from the Rate of Climb Indicator—look out—is the ball in the middle showing that we are

properly balanced and not climbing sideways—look out—how are the engine temperatures and pressures doing? Getting accustomed to this kind of procedure may seem wearisome at first, like practising scales on the piano. It certainly doesn't leave much time for admiring the view. (In fact during the whole early part of my training I don't think I even noticed that there was a view). But after a while, provided you keep at it conscientiously (or are bullied into it) it becomes a natural habit, a part of flying.

The instruments during a climb

The nose attitude during a climb

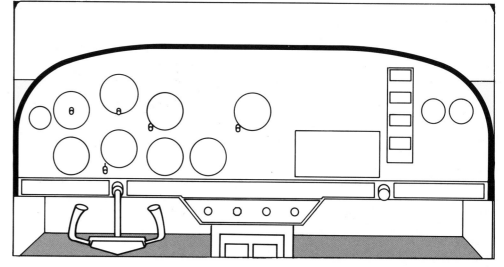

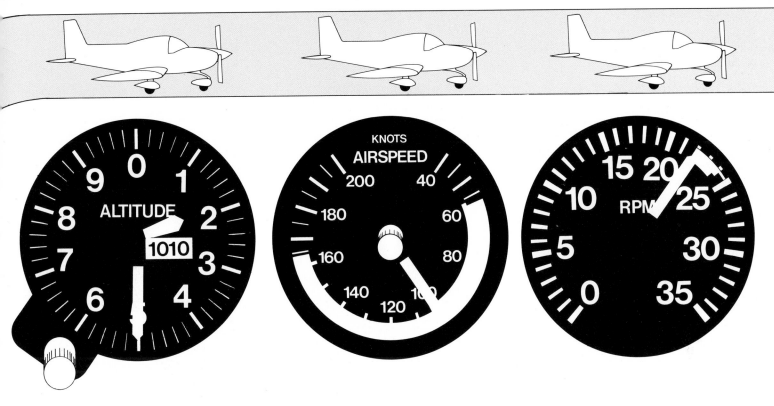

The nose attitude when flying level and the instruments

How do we stop the climb and get back to level flight at 100 knots? This is the exception to the P-A-T rule. It is A for Attitude first.

We shall have half an eye on the Altimeter all the time as we come up to the desired height. Twenty feet below (one mark on the dial) we simply lower the nose to the normal level position. The aircraft takes a little time to react and will still climb that last twenty feet even if the nose is put down, so with this piece of anticipation we should be able to get it exactly on the chosen spot on the Altimeter.

We haven't touched the throttle so the aircraft is still on full power. Our task now is to hold her steady while the speed increases to 100 knots. As the speed builds up there will be more and more forward pressure needed on the control column to keep her level, because, once again, more speed means more lift. Just before the needle of the airspeed indicator comes up to 100 knots we can ease the throttle back to our cruising revs of 2200 to 2300, hold her there, check

whether she is happily straight and level, and trim. (To keep in balance it will probably be necessary to take off the bit of right rudder used at full power). This time P-A-T has turned into A-P-T, but it is the sole exception.

The reason is obvious. Bringing the power back to the cruise before levelling off from the climb would mean that the speed would drop right back so that it would take all day to struggle slowly up to cruising speed.

Forward pressure on column, then power back and trim

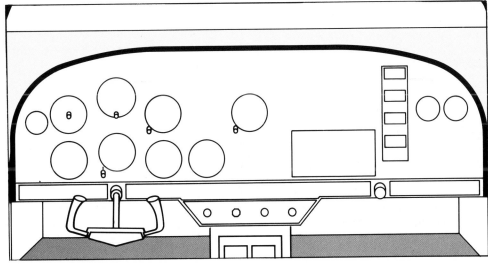

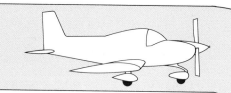

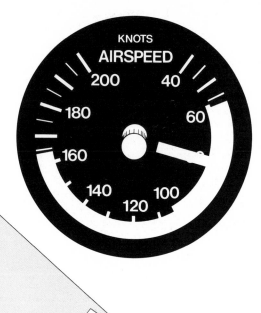

The descent

To get down again we tackled a basic gliding descent (throttle pulled right back so that the engine just ticks over and the propeller windmills happily) at 80 knots. As with climbing, the look out before beginning is vital. We don't want to descend on top of somebody, so it is important to look down below the nose and also backwards below the tail.

It is also necessary to look after the engine in a long glide. We met the carburettor heat control in the pre-take off checks. Closing the throttle and gliding is the time when aircraft engine carburettors are most prone to clogging with ice. It is a matter of elementary physics. Closing the throttle almost closes the butterfly valve in the carburettor. The air drawn in by the windmilling engine has to flow at a furious rate to get past the narrow restriction and in doing so there is a hefty loss of temperature. So the carburettor heat, (which brings warm air to the carburettor from around the exhaust manifold instead of introducing cold stuff direct from the outside) must be pulled right out before the glide and not pushed back in again until just before we are ready to use the engine again to level out. It is also recommended that we should warm the engine up with a burst of throttle every 500 feet, just to keep it at a working temperature; otherwise it might cough, splutter and die or be generally miserable about picking up when power is needed at the end of the descent.

So, from a straight and level cruise, we pull out the carb heat and then pull out the throttle, right back to the idle position. (Once more, a bit of rudder may be needed to stop the yaw over to the right). In the lovely silence which now ensues we hold the nose up by progressively pulling back on the control column and watch the speed come back to 80 knots. Having got around 80 to 85, we gently lower the nose to the attitude which will keep us at 80 and having found it, we trim

off what will by now be quite a heavy amount of backward pull on the stick. There we have it once more: Power, Attitude, Trim.

That little pause before lowering the nose to allow the speed to come back is the secret of a happy, controlled descent. If we pushed the nose down straight away from 100 knots we should go down at 100 knots. Being clever and slowing down to the speed we want is the equivalent of a motorist changing gear or applying brakes before entering a steep hill, rather than trying to get control of his speed half way down it.

Throttle right back, carburettor heat on

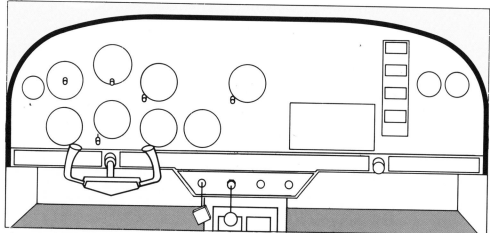

The descent: levelling off

Coming out of the descent needs more anticipation than levelling out from the climb. Gravity is helping the aircraft down. So this time we pick a point 100 feet above the chosen levelling off point to bring back the power (having previously shoved the carburettor heat back in). The nose will want to pitch up of its own accord as soon as we put on some throttle, but we need to discourage that and hold her down to let the speed pick up to the normal cruising 100 knots. Then we level out. All being well it takes about 100 feet for the speed to come up. So having levelled out we should find ourselves bowling along at the right height and at the right speed; which gives a feeling of great satisfaction when it comes off.

Increase power, 100ft above the levelling off point

As with most skills, experienced operators have their shortcuts. A pilot may know, for example, that to get his aircraft settled in a correct glide from the cruise all he has to do is close the throttle, give one—two—three—and a bit—turns on the trim wheel, and let her look after herself. I was not popular when I mentioned this. It is a bad habit to use the trim wheel to control the aircraft, I was told. 'Keep your hands away from that trim wheel and never use it except to take a load off the control column.'

We took off to practise these things on a beautiful calm evening, with the air silky and smooth. In spite of these ideal conditions I found things difficult. At first my climbing angle was too steep, with the aircraft struggling away, hanging on its propeller. Then it was too shallow, with the airspeed racing up into the nineties. I was committing the great sin of trimming too early, before the aircraft had settled down. The concentration, and indeed, bad temper, which these problems engendered meant that I forgot other vital things, like lowering the nose on the climb to make sure that nothing was happening ahead. I also went for P-A-T levelling off from the climb on one occasion, bringing the power back to the cruising revs before levelling off, with the result that the aeroplane floundered about at eighty knots and never even reached its appointed altitude. We did climbs of 900 feet, followed by descents of 900 feet. Coming down was a bit more competent than going up, but not much. The aeroplane seemed to insist on gliding at 75, rather than 80. Once more, it was a case of trimming too early. I was also putting her into the glide with a sharp forward lunge of the control column, instead of merely just releasing some of the back pressure and lowering her down gently, like putting a kitten in a basket. All these shortcomings were pointed out to me quite sharply when we got back on the ground. Also I was told to spend less time glueing my eyes to the instruments and more time looking around to see what was happening outside. Not a good day. Though maybe it was time for the statutory jab of anti-over confidence medicine.

Chapter 9: Coming down

The descent is, of course, just the first part of the treat which is in store called the Landing. We can get away with some rough and ready climbing. But a descent to a runway is a precision job. We shall have endless trouble with landing unless we learn how to get the aeroplane down to just the right height above a spot at the end of the runway at the right speed. This would be a ghastly proposition if we had to judge where to close the throttle and begin a descent in a straight line which would bring us exactly to where we wanted to be. But we don't have to do this (although good luck to those who demonstrate that they can manage it). By using flap

or power, or both at once, we can vary the rate of descent on the way down, according to how we see our approach shaping up. Getting used to doing this is the first stage in tackling the approach to landing.

There was, firstly, one more item to add to my store of airmanship before tackling the exercise. In climbing we learned about the height restriction imposed by the London Terminal Control Area. (Restrictions may well exist in other forms over other training airfields). There is also a restriction at the lower end called 'the 500 foot Rule', which states that you must not fly closer than 500 foot to any person, vessel, vehicle or structure. That means within 500 feet of the ground in this country, for all intents and purposes. The ground around our training area is about 300 feet above sea level, so in practising descents we should not go lower than about 800 feet on an Altimeter set to the QNH. (For taking off or landing this rule doesn't apply, of course. Nor does it apply to flying policemen or people taking part in an

authorised air display). There is a separate height restriction for built-up areas, towns and cities. The rule is (i) to fly 1500 feet above the nearest object within 2000 feet of the aircraft, or (ii) to be at a sufficient height to clear the area safely without danger to people or property on the ground in the event of an engine failure, whichever is the higher. What this means, in effect, is that we shan't be doing any descent practice except over open country. There is another rule we should also know about. There must be no hanging around taking an aerial view of football matches or other entertainments. The law says that no aircraft should fly over or within 3000 feet of any open air assembly of more than 1000 persons. This became a reality for me when practising forced landings without power over what I took to be a bit of deserted heathland, only to see on closer inspection that a motor cycle scramble was taking place. I didn't count whether there were more or less a thousand people present. But I did see a police car, and so left. (I am told that a plea that I had no connection with the

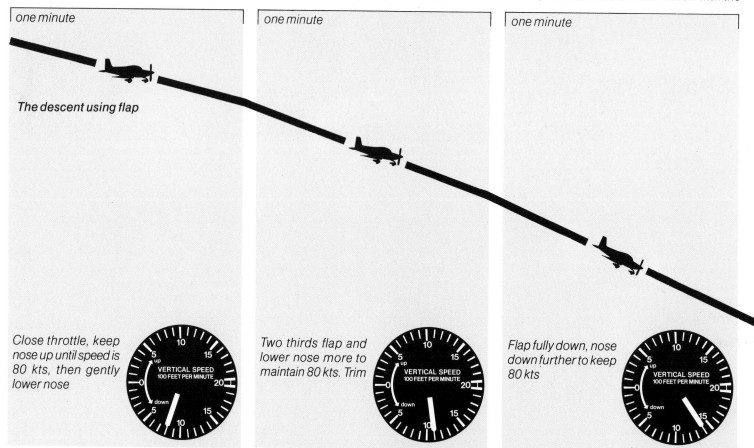

one minute

The descent using flap

Close throttle, keep nose up until speed is 80 kts, then gently lower nose

one minute

Two thirds flap and lower nose more to maintain 80 kts. Trim

one minute

Flap fully down, nose down further to keep 80 kts

event and did not even know it was taking place would have been an acceptable defence).

We begin by looking at what the use of flap does. Once again it is P-A-T.

P having had a look out and down we enter the glide in the normal way by closing the throttle, holding the nose up until the speed comes back to 80 knots and then gently lowering it to keep that speed. If we have a look at the Vertical Speed Indicator (VSI) we shall see that it is registering a descent of about 800 feet per min. Now, lower two thirds flap. If we kept the nose attitude the same the speed would drop (extra drag). So to keep 80 knots we lower it.

A lower nose to maintain 80 knots.

T Trim. The rate of descent has now gone up to 1100 feet per min.

Putting down the last stage of flap creates even more drag, so we have to put the nose down even further to keep our 80 knots. The result will be a rate of descent (ROD) of as much as 1400 feet per minute. That is almost double the descent rate with no flap, so there is plenty of adjustment possible on that final approach to land. We can lose height quite rapidly if need be.

But supposing we are more interested in flattening the approach and reducing the rate of descent? That is where Power comes in. The effect is the opposite to flap.

P enter the glide as usual. No flap. No power, engine just ticking over. Rate of descent 800 feet per min. Now, put on some throttle and bring the power up to a modest 1500 revs.

A if we kept the nose steady the speed would go up. So we raise the nose up far enough to keep 80 knots (we shall find that it will want to come up of its own accord, so we let it do just that).

T trim her at 80 knots. We shall now be showing a rate of descent of around 400 feet per min., half the height loss in the normal glide descent.

Increasing the power still more will lessen the descent proportionally. Keeping 80 knots at 2000 revs will involve no descent at all, the aircraft may even climb a bit. Full Power at 80 knots is, of course, a healthy climb, as we have seen.

Therefore, the more power the slower the descent, the more flap the quicker the descent. This is invaluable on the approach to a landing, because we can make adjustments all the way down, depending on the approach we need to make.

BUT, we do not keep making adjustments with the flaps. Once they are down, they stay down. It is far too clumsy to wag them up and down, up and down. The power, use of the throttle, will give us all the adjustment we need, even with the flaps down.

one minute

At 1500 rpm, raise the nose to keep 80 kts and trim

one minute

Increase in power proportionately lessens rate of descent

one minute

2000 rpm at 80 kts results in no descent, and may even start a climb

The descent using power

We shall test this out by doing a descent using both power and flap. From our cruise at 100 knots we close the throttle, keep the nose up in the usual way, letting the speed come back. Having got the airspeed down to well below 100 knots and the flap limiting speed, 90 knots will do nicely, we give her two thirds of flap, lowering the nose at the same time with nice smooth co-ordinated movement of the control column to get and keep 90 knots, although we needn't be too fussy about getting it spot on because we haven't finished yet. We then feed on a bit of power, about 1500 revs, raise the nose to maintain a steady 80 knots on the Airspeed Indicator and trim at that speed. We know that the rate of descent must be somewhere between what we had with two thirds flap alone (1100 feet per min) and what we had with 1500 revs alone (400 feet per min). In fact it comes out at something about 500 feet per min, which is much nearer the figure we got with power alone than the one we got with flap. Power is the stronger of the two. As they say: 'Power looks after you'.

The clue to it all is the grasp the fundamental truth that it is power that controls the rate of descent and the elevators which control the speed. If we are coming in too low it is the throttle we reach for (actually, we shall have our hand on it anyway). If we are coming in too fast it is the nose position which has to be corrected with the control column. The great beginners' fault is to see trees looming up a bit too close at the end of the runway and respond by picking the nose up to get out of their way. Wrong ... wrong ... wrong. All that will happen is that the speed will drop, which could mean a lot of trouble and a dramatic increase in the rate of descent in the immediate future. Changing height with power and speed with elevators on the descent is something that has got to enter the blood.

The only way to achieve that is to practice. We spent two long sessions working at this, doing pretend descents towards fields in the country. On the way down, Jeanne would say: 'No, I've changed my mind, not that field, make it that wood over there beyond it'. And I would have to make the necessary response, putting on power to reduce the descent in order to reach the new target. I would be settled down to that when she would say: 'No, I've changed my mind again. Back to the original field.' That would mean taking off the power and putting down more flap to steepen the descent enough to get into the first field.

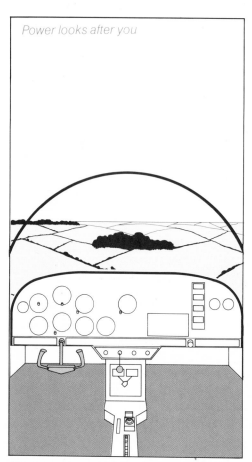

From a cruise at 100 kts, close throttle. Keep nose up to reduce speed to 90 kts

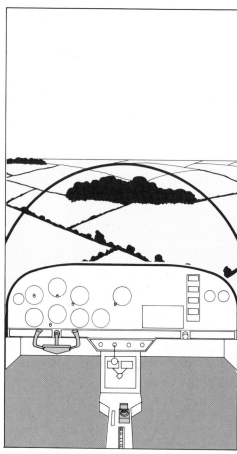

Give two thirds flap and use control column to get and keep 90 kts. ROD 1100ft per min.

To reduce descent, feed on power to 1500 rpm, raise nose to maintain 80 kts. ROD 500ft per min.

Then at around 600 feet above the ground (well away from built-up areas or herds of sensitive cattle) it was full throttle and away into the climb. With full flap down and the aircraft trimmed for the descent, this involved quite a strong backwards heave on the control column. The flaps have to be brought up in stages, and the aircraft doesn't show any particular interest in climbing until the third giving biggest flap angle is up. With two thirds she settles down to a laborious ascent, but it isn't until we put the second third up that she begins to feel at all happy about gaining height. When she is well on her way up again we remove the remaining third, attempting to anticipate and remove that sinking feeling as they come up. This climb away from a full flap glide is a useful exercise on its own, called the Missed Approach. It is what is involved if we have to abandon an approach to land for some reason. (We don't

like the look of how it is shaping up or we are instructed to go round again by air traffic control because something is obstructing the runway).

On the second day of this we came back to the airfield and I was allowed to try some real landing approaches from 1000 feet to see how it felt. This involved beginning the descent at right angles to the runway, on the so-called 'base leg' (more about this when we come to circuits), and then turning in towards the field at the right moment. On the final part I was able to judge for myself whether to put on power or take it off, according to whether the end of the runway seemed to be crawling up the windscreen (we were too low) or disappearing below the nose (too high). On the very last stage we put down all the flap and instead of keeping to our 80 knots, allowing the speed to settle

to 70 knots, which is the speed for doing the actual landing. (At 80 knots she wouldn't be ready to come down and would float to the other end of the runway before touching down). Then would come my first inkling of the landing procedure, as Jeanne took over the controls and I followed through. 'I'm going to stop her landing for as long as possible ... stop her ... stop her ... back a bit more ... don't land ... don't land ...'. Until finally, with a gentle squidge of rubber, the aircraft subsided onto the runway. She made it seem easy.

One thing I noticed was that if the aeroplane was properly settled down and trimmed on the approach I hardly needed to use the control column at all. Putting on a touch of power would raise the nose automatically and keep the speed right. Taking off power would lower it. She knows what she is doing.

To steepen descent again involves taking off power and putting down more flap

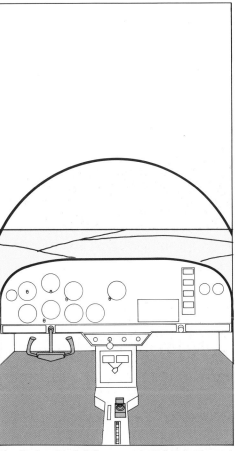

A climb with full flap needs full throttle and backwards pressure on column. Flaps are brought up in stages

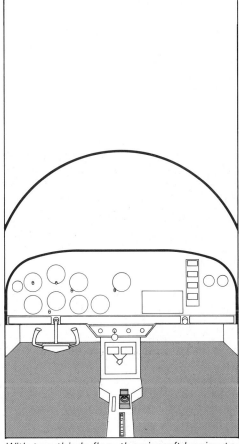

With two thirds flap, the aircraft begins to climb. At one third, gains height easily. When settled to climb, remove last third

Chapter 10: And now the turn

I had been turning left and right when the need arose by putting on a bit of gentle, hesitant bank and letting the aeroplane waft round of its own accord. Even I knew that this was a watered-down version of the crisp manoeuvres Jeanne executed when she took us round a corner. We went to the briefing room to discuss the real thing.

The object was to turn the aircraft onto any chosen heading while remaining at a constant height using up to 30 degrees of bank. This involved meeting the instrument which tells what 30 degrees of bank is: the Artificial Horizon, first mentioned in Chapter six.

The small bar in the middle, known as the aircraft symbol, tilts according to the position of the aircraft relative to the horizon, represented by the thin line across the dial. The bar can also go up above the horizon, showing a climb, or below it, for a descent. Thanks to the gyro inside the works the horizon will always stay fixed, parallel to the real horizon. It's the aeroplane which moves around it, taking the small bar imitating the aeroplane's wings with it. But at the moment we are more interested in what happens at the top of the dial. A pointer moves right or left across a series of graduated marks, standing for angles of bank, every time we raise or lower a wing. There are some heavy paint marks on the dial, representing 30 degrees and 60 degrees of bank. In between 0 and 30 degrees are two lighter paint marks, representing 10 and 20 degrees. For the medium turn we want the pointer on the first thick mark. Thirty degrees is classed as a medium turn.

There is also some airmanship to consider. Looking out before a turn is once more vital. So is looking out during the turn and while rolling out of it. We always start by looking out in the opposite direction to the way we are turning, so that the final, most

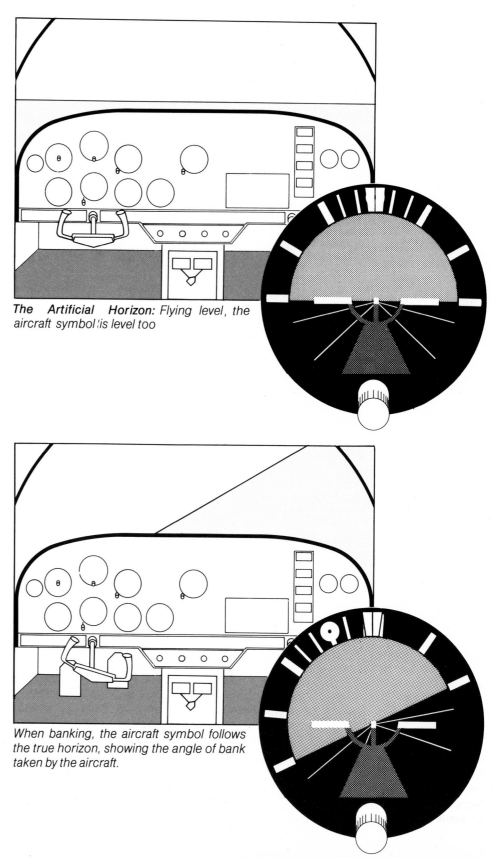

The Artificial Horizon: Flying level, the aircraft symbol is level too

When banking, the aircraft symbol follows the true horizon, showing the angle of bank taken by the aircraft.

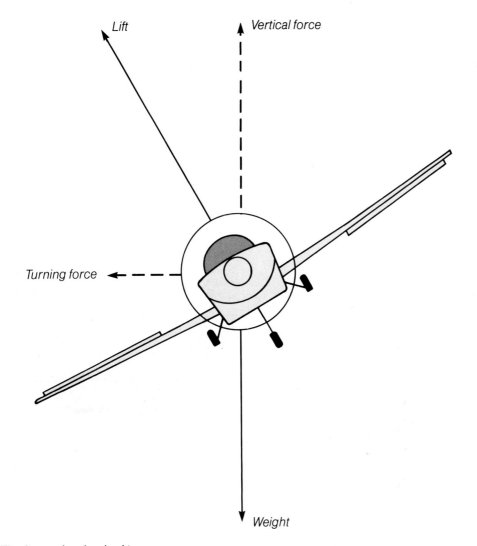

Lift

Vertical force

Turning force

Weight

The forces in a banked turn

want to do that? A small diagram on the blackboard explained all.

In level flight the lift of the wings exactly equals the weight of the aircraft and load. But if the aircraft is banked to 30 degrees the equation is upset. The lift is still at right angles to the wings, but it is no longer pulling directly against gravity. As it is inclined to one side of the vertical, there is no longer enough upward force to balance the weight. So a little pressure is needed on the control column to raise the nose. The effect is to increase the angle of attack of the wings, which provides a portion more lift. It does so at the expense of speed—the extra load of drag will pull the speed back to about 95 knots from the 100 knots at which the turn was started. This could be compensated by putting on some more power, but for a medium turn of 30 degrees it isn't worth the trouble. A loss of 5 knots is not going to bother us too much. (When we come to do steeper turns with more bank requiring more backward pressure we *shall* be putting on some extra power, but that is for later).

During the turn we indulge in the visual in-out-in-out routine that we met with climbing. First checking that the bank is correct on the Artificial Horizon, then looking out, then checking the balance, looking out, checking altitude, looking out, always keeping one eye on the Direction Indicator to watch progress towards the chosen heading.

Getting out of the turn is simply a matter of rolling the wings level. As they roll level the back pressure on the control column can be dispensed with, as can the rudder pressure. Picking the right moment to level the wings involves the art of anticipation once more. All the time the wings are banked the aircraft will keep turning. In the time it takes to level them from a medium turn she can go through about ten degrees on the compass. So we start rolling out about ten degrees before reaching the target (or heading) we are aiming for.

With experience, picking the right amount of bank and the correct back pressure and rudder becomes automatic. Instead of worrying about the instruments we can judge our turn from the look of the horizon. But there is a problem with side-by-side seating as found

up-to-date look takes in the bit of sky into which we are about to fly the aeroplane. With a high wing aircraft like the Cessna 150 it is considered good airmanship to raise the wing that we about to lower, to make sure that it is not concealing another aircraft from view. (The high wing will come down and blank off the area we are moving towards during the turn itself).

The chances are that we will get disorientated, which is a polite word for 'lost', while practising the turns unless we pick a good reliable landmark to help us keep track of our position. (The faithful reservoirs in the Lea Valley will come in useful here). Also, a series of turns can upset a Direction Indicator in poor condition, so we have to remember to

reset it to the compass before we use it to head for home. (And wait until the compass itself has settled down before we do so).

The procedure, having done the necessary look out, is to roll the aeroplane gently to 30 degrees, at the same time applying a bit of rudder in the direction we are going. This keeps the aeroplane in balance and stops the nose skidding away. Too much rudder and the aircraft will skid away from the turn. But experience, and the ball in the centre of the Turn and Slip Indicator, will tell us when we have it right. Having arrived at 30 degrees it is time to centralise the ailerons (to prevent over-banking) and to ease the control column back slightly to keep the nose up and prevent the aircraft from descending. Why should it in the Cheetah. Left hand turns and right hand turns look different, as the following diagrams demonstrate.

The problem is that with side-by-side seating a left or right bank will put each seat above or below the centre line. This means that the pilot will either be below his normal position relative to the nose, or above it. Sitting in the left seat the nose will therefore look unexpectedly low down, under the horizon, in a right bank. In a left bank the nose will look high, as though we were climbing. (In a single seater or a plane like the Chipmunk in which the seats are in tandem this doesn't apply, of course).

When demonstrated in the air the 30 degrees medium turn felt unexpectedly steep and was certainly a great deal steeper than anything I had done before. One bad habit needed eradicating straight away. The proper way to handle any banked turn is to lean into it, rather as a motor cyclist leans into the turns. I found myself edging away from the ground beyond the lowered wing. Instead of relaxing and going with the bank I was tensing up and leaning towards the middle of the aircraft; a case of nervousness brought about by the unfamiliar attitude.

This was put right for me by Jeanne demonstrating a really steep turn, a full 60 degrees angle of bank, which involved twice as much bank, extra power and appreciable back pressure on the control column to keep the machine flying. After one of those, 30 degrees seemed quite mild.

Several faults and bad habits cropped up:

1 Jerking the machine into the bank with a violent thrust of the control column, instead of easing her in gently.

2 Not giving enough backward pressure on the control column once the 30 degree bank has been reached, with the result that the nose drops, the speed picks up and the level turn disintegrates into a spiral dive.

3 Over-cooking it, giving her too much back pressure, so that the level turn became a gentle climbing turn, with the speed dropping back to the eighties. This fault developed in particular when doing right

The pilot's view of a right and left turn

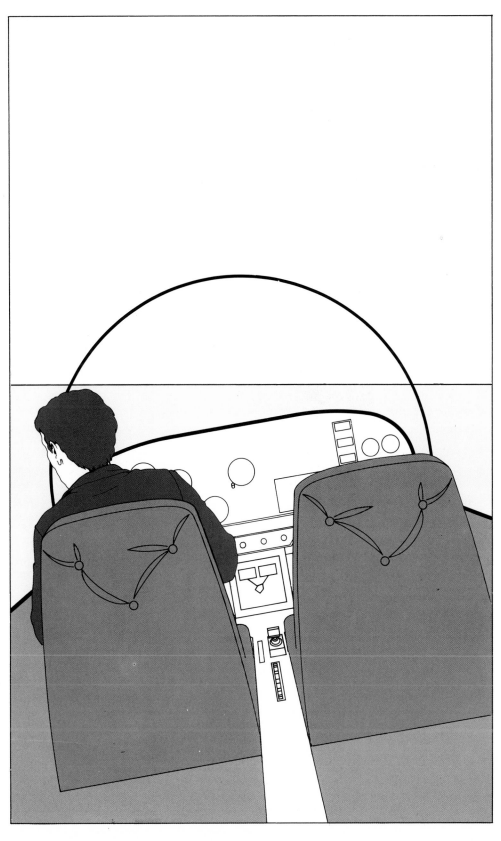

hand turns, in which the nose looks lower than normal anyway. Check the instruments.

4 Not anticipating the end of the turn soon enough, so that I went past the chosen heading and had to do a surreptitious bank in the other direction to get her on course.

5 Getting so engrossed in the technique of the business that I forgot to look out before beginning the turn, during the turn and before rolling out.

Having mastered getting in and out of the turn we did some complete circles, 360 degrees round the compass, rolling out on precisely the heading on which we had started the turn, and if possible, at the same height. This is a chance to practice the routine of keeping a good look out during the turns, coming inside to check one instrument at a time to make sure that all is well with height, balance, speed and angle of bank. Also, of course, keeping an eye on how the Direction Indicator is coming along.

Controlling the amount of bank with the control column became automatic after a while. I began with hesitant jerks. That is not the right way to do it, I was told. What is needed is a gentle but confident movement of the yoke, holding it steady while the bank develops and then, just before the correct angle is reached, centralising the ailerons to check the bank and maintain it.

The next stage was to climb and descend while turning, which seemed at first a lot to take on simultaneously, particularly when asked to level out from a climb and straighten out from a turn at the same time.

In a climbing turn only 15 degrees of bank is used, otherwise the climb rate would suffer. In descending turns close to the ground (such as the turn towards the runway on the final approach to land) not more than 20 degrees is used.

On the final run into the airfield I did a gliding turn in the circuit, which involved putting the nose down to keep the gliding speed at 80 knots during the bank. Gliding close to the ground is one time when losing 5 knots of speed COULD bother us, but that is another story to be explained later.

Chapter 11:
Aerial calamities: the stall

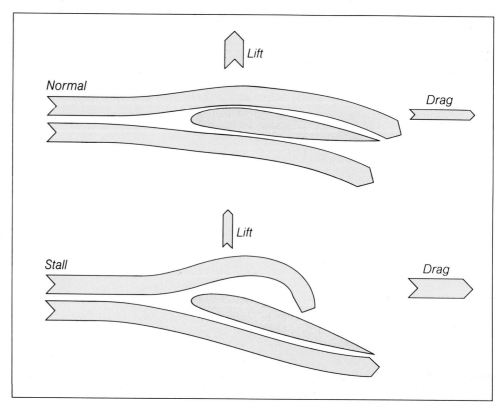

The airflow over the wing in a stall

The aerial calamity known as 'the Stall' is normally classed among the deadly sins to be avoided by virtuous aviators. So why flirt with it by devoting a whole lesson to stalling? It's a form of inoculation. To experience the beginning of a stall is to know one for ever more. After learning what it feels like we should never get caught unawares. At the same time we can learn how to recover from a stall without losing too much height if we *do* get caught.

But first, what is a stall? And what causes it?

It happens when the wings give up providing controllable lift and simply down tools and strike. They only do this under extreme provocation. It occurs when the angle at which the wings meet the airflow (known, as we have discovered in Chapter three, as the 'angle of attack') is too steep for the air to slip smoothly over the wing surfaces. Instead of sliding neatly above and below the wing the air starts breaking down in swirls and eddies on the top rear wing surface; unless something is done about correcting the attitude of the aeroplane the condition soon spreads to the whole upper wing surface. As a result that part of the lift which comes from the 'suction effect' of the lower pressure on top of the wings is greatly decreased. The nose drops and down she goes.

Marked in the *Technical Notes* or Handbook for every aeroplane is a 'stalling speed'. This is the airspeed at which, at a given weight, and without power, the aeroplane will stop flying like a bird and behave more like a brick. It is 55 knots for the Cheetah, without flap. (The extra lift given by using two thirds of flap brings it down to 50 knots). This is slightly misleading, as speed, or the lack of it, is not in fact the prime culprit. The point is

that at these low speeds, without power, the aeroplane will be inclined to sink through shortage of lift. This means that the wings will be meeting an onrush of air (or 'relative airflow') coming slightly from below. The angle at which a wing meets the airflow is what determines its 'angle of attack', and a steep angle of attack caused by airflow coming up from below is the real cause of all the trouble.

The aerodynamics of all this is explained and illustrated in the text books, notably in the chapter on stalling in Vol 1 of *Flight Briefing for Pilots*. For my edification Jeanne also drew a simple graph on the briefing room blackboard, showing how, to start with, lift increases as the angle of attack increases, until an angle of about 16 degrees, when lift flattens and then decreases rapidly.

Bringing about a deliberate stall for practice purposes involves reining in the aeroplane to what feels like a near standstill in mid air. We close the throttle (as usual, there may be a bit of yaw to check as the power comes off) and keep bringing back the control column to

see how long we can keep her flying straight and level. As the speed comes back, even more back pressure on the control column is needed. Everything goes quiet, until just above stalling speed what are quaintly called 'the incipient symptoms' arrive. At about 65 knots the stall warning sounds, which on the Cheetah is a wavering high-pitched buzz. (It is set off by the small tab projecting from the leading edge of the wing which we met during the pre-flight checks. As the angle of attack increases, the airflow creeps under the tab, forces it upwards and sets off the electrical buzzer.) Ignoring the buzz we press on to what is called 'light buffeting'. This means that we are nearly at the stall. The buffeting is caused by the turbulent eddies of air generated by the partly stalled wings setting up a flutter back along the aircraft, like a boat's sail that has lost the wind, and striking the elevators. You can feel the buffet through the control column.

One other thing we shall notice is that as the stall is approached the whole aircraft feels sloppy and unstable. The controls will have noticably reduced effect.

There will be no doubt about when the stall happens. The buffeting moves from 'light' to 'heavy', and the nose drops down. What then? To recover we need some speed in order to be able to control the aeroplane. So we make a timely simultaneous movement of throttle and control column, the throttle in to full power and the control column forward. When all the buffeting and buzzing has stopped we can use the ailerons to level the wings—if necessary—and ease the control column gently back to put the aeroplane into a normal climb. We can do this recovery at any time, without waiting for the full stall and nose drop. We shall be practising recoveries from various stages: from the first sound of the buzzer, the first sign of buffet and the final nose drop. The earlier it's done the less height is lost.

Apart from that one or other of the wings may drop. In such a case I was warned NEVER to try to use the ailerons to bring it back up again, because it will only aggravate the situation. The model was produced to show why. A wing drops because it is not flying well; i.e. the air is not flowing smoothly over the wing because the angle of attack is too great. Putting the aileron down to bring the wing up again effectively *increases* the angle of attack still more. So over she goes into a probable spin, helped over by the other wing which is still flying reasonably well. With the Cheetah I was told that you can probably get away with using the ailerons at the near-stall, but it is not a good habit to get into, because if you are flying an aeroplane close to the ground that does not take to that sort of behaviour then you've really got trouble. So make it a golden rule to leave the ailerons alone in such a case.

So how do we steady her if she begins to drop a wing? The main thing is to check the yaw that is bound to follow. If the right wing has gone down, a touch of left rudder will prevent that happening and may be all that is needed to level the aircraft. Too much rudder and a yaw to the left may provoke the other wing to stall and drop in the process. Stop the yaw and remove the risk of spinning, even if you have to let the wing hang down, carry on with the recovery from the stall and level the wings when there is enough speed to use the ailerons. BUT NEVER USE THE AILERONS BEFORE.

But before going off to try it there was a new set of checks to learn: the H.A.S.E.L.L. checks. HASELL is used to prepare for any manoeuvre involving a sudden loss of height, notably in stalling and spinning.

H stands for Height: It is common sense to make sure that we begin from high enough to be able to pull out at a safe height above the ground.

A — Airframe: Do we want flaps or don't we? (We shall be trying some stalls with and some without). The brakes should be off because in some aircraft they restrict movement of the rudder pedals.

S — Security: Are the harnesses and the hatches secure, and have all loose articles been stowed away? (Pushing the control column forward to recover could encourage hard objects on the back seat to fly forward hitting the pilot on the head).

E — Engine: Bring the carburettor heat out to make sure we haven't picked up any ice, check the fuel contents, make sure mixture is at rich, have a look at the temperatures and pressures, then push the carb heat back to cold.

L — Location: We should perform our manoeuvres away from built-up areas, clear of cloud and far away from any active airfield.

L — Lookout: This comes last, because we need the freshest look. To make sure there is no unsuspecting pilot below we need to make turns through ninety degrees, left and right, so that the whole area beneath the aircraft is covered.

My main fault when it came to doing the exercise was being too slow with the recovery. The throttle should go in and the control column should go forward IMMEDIATELY the nose drops. A slight hesitation means the unnecessary loss of several hundred feet of height. But my first problem was to overcome a built-in resistance to allowing the machine to stall in the first place. It seemed all wrong to keep holding that stick back while the machine flopped through the air becoming more and more difficult to control. Just before the actual moment of the break she seemed to be hanging motionless

with an eerie feeling of stillness, broken only by the mournful protest of the stall warning buzzer. With all that happening I found it difficult not to keep edging the stick forward to stave off the big drop. When it came it was not, in fact, a particularly violent drop in the Cheetah. Every aircraft has different stall characteristics. (One of the essential ways of getting to know a new type is to see how it behaves in the stall). Having tried some recoveries after the so-called 'nose drop', we experimented by recovering earlier—at the buzzer and at the first sign of buffeting.

By taking steps to stop the process at this early stage it was possible to get the machine flying healthily again with scarcely any loss of height at all. I then tried one with full flap on and found that the whole process became more sudden and more violent. With the flaps hanging down the speed dropped off much more suddenly. The stall warning hardly had time to buzz before the nose broke away, and this time it really was quite a violent drop. I now had three things to do simultaneously: as well as the control column forward and full power I had to bring a third of the flap up. How do you do these three things at once with only two hands? Jeanne showed me a trick which was to prove useful in a number of manoeuvres which called for raising some of the flap and putting on full power simultaneously (such as when overshooting from a landing). You flick the flap switch forward to the 'up' position as you bring your right hand through to the throttle knob. Having pushed the throttle right in you bring your hand back again to the flap switch and flick it back to the middle (or 'stop') position. If you can manage to judge about three seconds for the whole process, presto! You will have raised one third of flap, which will help the aircraft to start climbing. I practised this technique so that I could do it without having to look down to where the flap switch was. It was to come in very useful later when doing 'touch-and-goes' (landing and then opening the throttle immediately to take off again) during circuit training.

Take good note of that sudden, violent stall during a glide with full flap on, I was warned. It imitated the circumstances of a stall when on final landing approach. If it happened then, the result could be nasty. Keeping the speed right will ensure it never does.

Chapter 12:
Aerial calamities: spinning

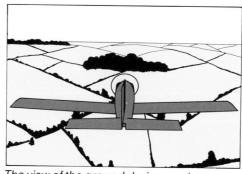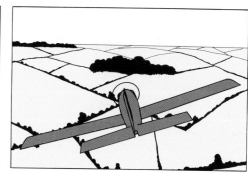

The view of the ground during a spin

Spinning

There is no point in pretending that sitting in a spinning aircraft is everyone's idea of entertainment. As spinning time comes along your instructor will either become gentle and solicitous or brusque and hearty, depending on his or her character. Jeanne related to me her own bad experience of spinning for the first time. Her instructor suddenly threw the machine into a spin without warning her what was about to happen. This is the short, sharp, shock method and is not nowadays recommended. It can lead to an unpleasant and frightening moment. Even with her own soft approach Jeanne has had students who have sat taut and terrified during the whole spinning procedure.

But spinning is taught in Britain because it is felt to be important that everyone should recognise what a spin is; be aware of what causes it in order to avoid getting into one unawares; and know how to stop a spin quickly if they find themselves in one. To these worthy reasons I would add another. Being able to get out of a spin calmly and neatly is a great boost to the confidence. It becomes a pleasure.

My own experience is probably typical. The morning I woke up and looked out at a clear sky with no cloud and perfect visibility I began to feel slight butterflies in my stomach. It was a perfect spinning day, and I knew what was going to be in store for me when I turned up at the airfield. I had spun once before, when a friend put his aircraft into a spin suddenly while demonstrating a stall. It was a fairly harrowing moment. I had no idea what the aircraft was doing, or why. All I could see was the ground twirling round in front of the windscreen. I dragged my eyes

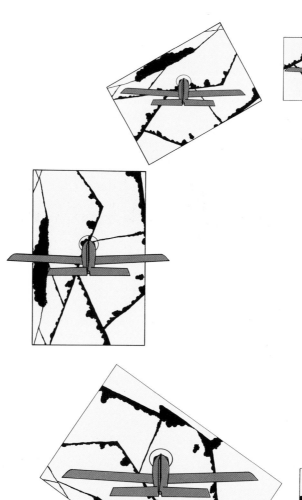

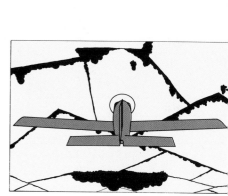

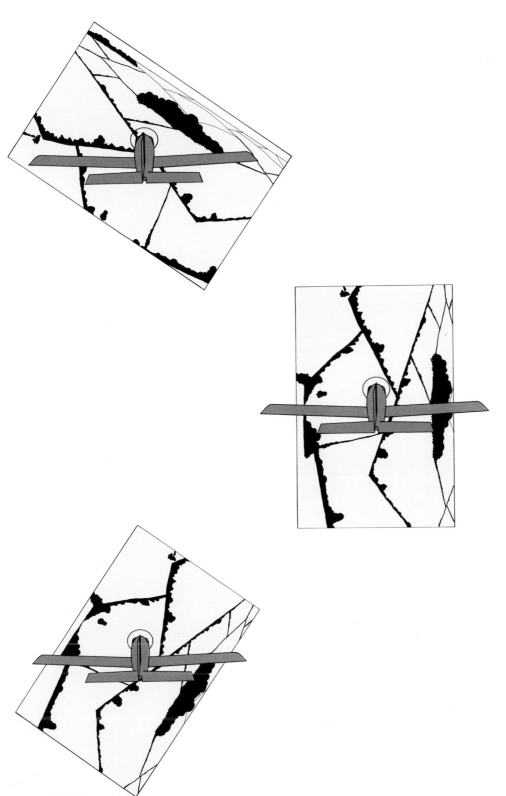

away from that and became aware of one of the Instruments (it must have been the Direction Indicator) gyrating round the dial like a top. At the same time I was being flung about the cockpit in an undignified fashion, frantically reaching out for something solid to hang on to. My friend knew what he was doing, but I didn't know that he knew. I was physically and morally shaken when he pulled us out. It could have put me off the whole thing for life.

So I wasn't expecting to enjoy it, though I had made a tense resolution to grit my teeth and bear it. But after a careful explanation of what exactly is going on I became less worried. The great break-through came when I realised that it is not necessary to gaze, horrified, at the extraordinary exhibition going on outside the windscreen. It is better to concentrate on what you know the aircraft is doing, feel part of her, live in your own universe inside the cockpit and feel the way she responds to your corrective movements. From the moment I discovered this, spinning became an interesting and even enjoyable experience. (I speak as someone who will never set foot on a roller coaster or Big Dipper).

First of all, what causes it? It happens when an aircraft stalls and yaws simultaneously. As the book has it: 'Stall plus Yaw equals Spin.' It can be achieved by banging in some rudder just before the point of stall. As the nose swings round, the inside (slower) wing, as would be expected, drops. This down-going wing now meets an upward airflow, which stalls it. The outside wing, moving faster (see Chapter eleven) keeps some lift. In addition, because it is going upwards the airflow is coming from above, the equivalent of lessening its angle of attack. The upper wing therefore keeps on flying, while the lower wing doesn't. The fully stalled wing has more drag than its part-stalled or even unstalled brother, and this perpetuates the yaw. The result is that the forces of nature take over completely and produce auto-rotation, or the spin. How do we get out of it? By stopping the yaw, the root of the evil. We shall come to that.

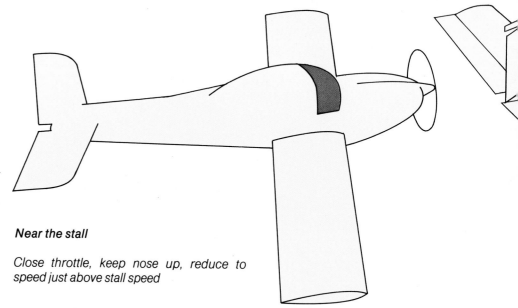

Checks prior to spinning exercise

1 Complete H.A.S.E.L.L. checks
2 The aircraft must be able to recover by 3000ft
3 Keep well away from control zones, built-up areas or airfields.
4 Everything in the aircraft must be fastened down
5 The aircraft must be cleared for spinning
6 Make sure there are no other aircraft near

Near the stall

Close throttle, keep nose up, reduce to speed just above stall speed

Spinning exercise

Before we try it there are certain precautions which have to be taken. First, there are the H.A.S.E.L.L. checks which we met in stalling.

Secondly, the rule here is no spinning if we can't recover by 3000 ft. This means that we are going to have to practise it some distance away, outside the London Terminal Control Area, so that we can start our spin from about 4000 ft. (No climbing above 2500 ft in the LTCA). We must also be well away from other people's control zones, built-up areas or active airfields. We want to be alone. There must be no cloud for us to suddenly fall through, and everything in the aircraft must be tied down so that it does not fly about knocking us on the head.

Also, the aircraft we use must be cleared for spinning practice, which the AA5A we normally use is not. So we are taking the School's faithful Cessna 150 Aerobat, which is kept purely for spinning.

The C150 seems a more crude and cramped machine than the AA5A: instructor and student are squashed closer together. The wing is above us, which makes downward visibility easier. But in turning it is necessary to lift a wing up slightly with a rolling action in order to do a proper look-out to left and right. It seems odd to be able to see a wheel just below my left elbow.

We set course to the north west, up through a gap in the hills and out of the London zone. We inform Luton what we are up to. Before

spinning the exercise calls for us to do a clean stall and a recovery, so that we can discover for ourselves what the aircraft's stalling speed is. We do one, and find the C150 'breaks' at 45 mph (her Airspeed Indicator is in mph). For spinning we pick a speed just above the stall for banging in the rudder for yaw, so we will do it at 55 mph.

Having done a careful look-out (turning the aircraft ninety degrees each way to make absolutely sure there is nothing in the vicinity) we close the throttle, keep the nose up and let the speed come back as quietness descends, just as in the stall. Then we do something which seems a gross and deliberate affront to all we have learned. We pull the control column back into our chest and give hard right rudder.

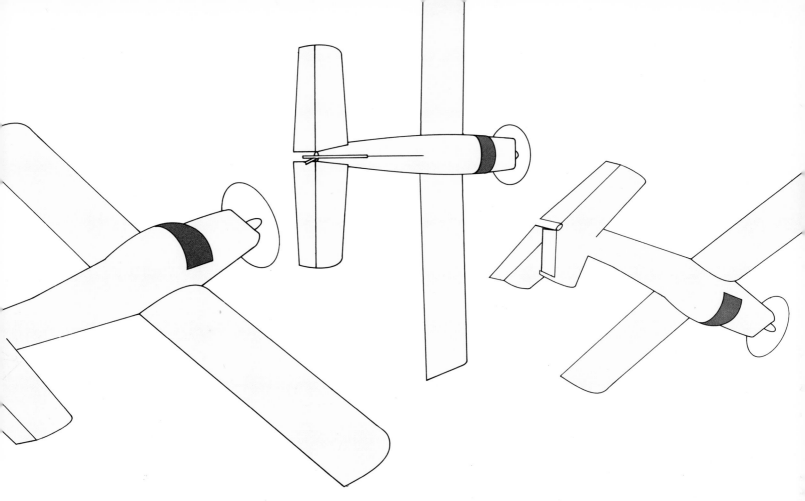

Pull control column back and press right rudder pedal

The yaw to the right results in a roll

The nose drops and the spin begins

Up comes the nose, at such an angle that the aircraft, already near the stalling speed, loses interest in flying and gets ready to stall. At the same time the sharp rudder action yaws the nose round to the right. So we have a pitch, a yaw, and because we get roll with yaw as a 'further effect', we get that too. And because we hold the controls in this uncouth position, we go on having it. The nose drops, the right wing drops, the left wing picks up a bit of lift and the spin has begun.

Of course, it doesn't have to happen in this carefully engineered way. If you fly badly enough, it can happen suddenly when you are not expecting it. But you have to fly very badly. For instance, supposing you were in the process of making a gliding approach to an airfield. You haven't judged your right turn

into the runway very well, so at a low airspeed you end up making a fairly sharp turn in order to arrive facing the end of the runway. During the turn, in your enthusiasm to get round, you have been a bit heavy with the rudder pedal, the effect of which is to make the nose yaw round to the right. Sitting in the left hand seat you see the nose well below the horizon at this point. Forgetting everything you have been taught, you try to pull the nose back to a healthy position again with an instinctive reaction, and grab back the control column. That merely brings the stall nearer by increasing the angle of attack of the wings. The downward, inside wing will stop flying first, and the spin will begin. Very nasty (and one reason why it is never advisable to make low speed turns near the ground without enough height to recover).

Nor do you have to be gliding with engine throttled back to spin. As we shall find out, a steep turn of 60 degrees needs a lot of back pressure on the control column (and a lot of power) to give the wings enough lift to keep the aircraft flying. The stalling speed is therefore raised, in a steep turn, to something like 70 mph in a Cessna 150. If the pilot is then too heavy with the rudder in an effort to stop the nose yawing down, i.e. bangs on top rudder causing an upward yaw and skidding movement, the controls are once more all set up for a spin. The upper wing can stop flying, the machine can then flip over and spin in the opposite direction to the way it was turning only a few moments earlier, which will give any pilot something to work out. Which is why the instruments need to be scanned carefully in a steep turn.

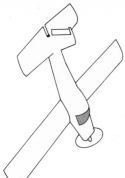

Spin recovery

Full left rudder

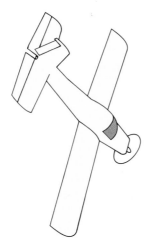

Stick forward

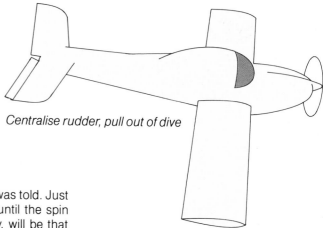

Centralise rudder, pull out of dive

Stopping spin

How do we stop a full spin once we are in it? Simply by curing the things which caused it, yaw plus stall.

In practice we are likely to know which way we are spinning, having just closed the throttle and applied a bootful of left or right rudder to get it all going. But a glance at the turn needle of the Turn and Slip indicator will soon tell us. It will be right on the stop in the direction of the spin. To stop it we just have to shove on full rudder in the opposite direction. In our practice spin we take off our right foot and jam down our left one.

At the same time we need to stop the stall in the normal way, by lowering the nose. So we push the control column forward. Don't

make a huge forward lunge, I was told. Just ease it forward progressively until the spin stops. The result, miraculously, will be that the earth will stop rotating round the wind-screen. As soon as it does we bring the rudder pedals back into the central position. Ahead will be the ground, indicating that we are in a dive, rapidly picking up flying speed. So it is a matter of gently easing the stick back, bringing the nose up towards the horizon. As the horizon is reached you put on full power and climb away normally, having a good look out to see where you are climbing to, naturally. You can then sit back a bit and feel pleased.

Have a look at the Altimeter and see how much height has gone. You may have only gone through a couple of revolutions, but lost a thousand feet.

Having done one to the right Jeanne let me try one to the left (some aeroplanes spin more easily one way than the other). After several I was able to have a look at what the instruments were showing during the spin. The Direction Indicator was demented,

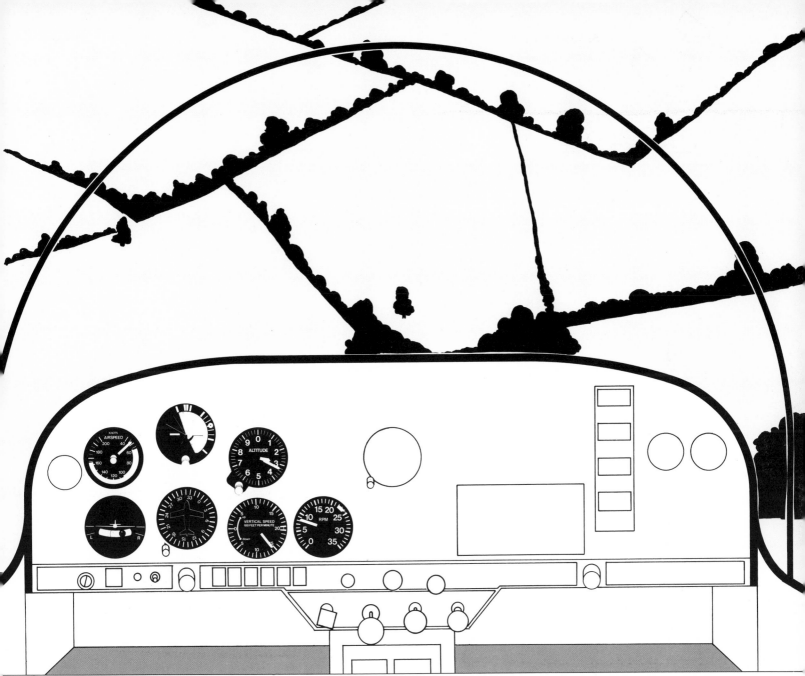

The instruments in a spin

showing a high rate of rotation round all points of the compass. The Vertical Speed Indicator and the Altimeter both showed that we were going down fast. The Airspeed Indicator was fluctuating at a low speed, evidence of our stalled position. The turn needle was on its stop and the ball was hard over on the other side, showing an outward skid. The illustration above shows a moment during a spin.

It is just possible that even the act of reading about it will make you feel queasy. Anyone feeling at all 'uncomfortable' (to use flying school euphemism) should warn their instructor in advance. Most schools have a standing order not to go on this exercise without a 'bag' at the ready, but well out of sight. Jeanne forgot ours until we were about to taxi away, so she left me in the plane while she returned to the school mut-

tering mysteriously about 'forgetting something'. When we came back from the exercise the total instructing staff appeared to be gathered in the operations room, grinning at me expectantly.

But no, we didn't use the bag. What had started as an apprehensive day for me turned out to be one of the most satisfying lessons yet. And a new trick learnt.

Chapter 13
Getting on the circuit

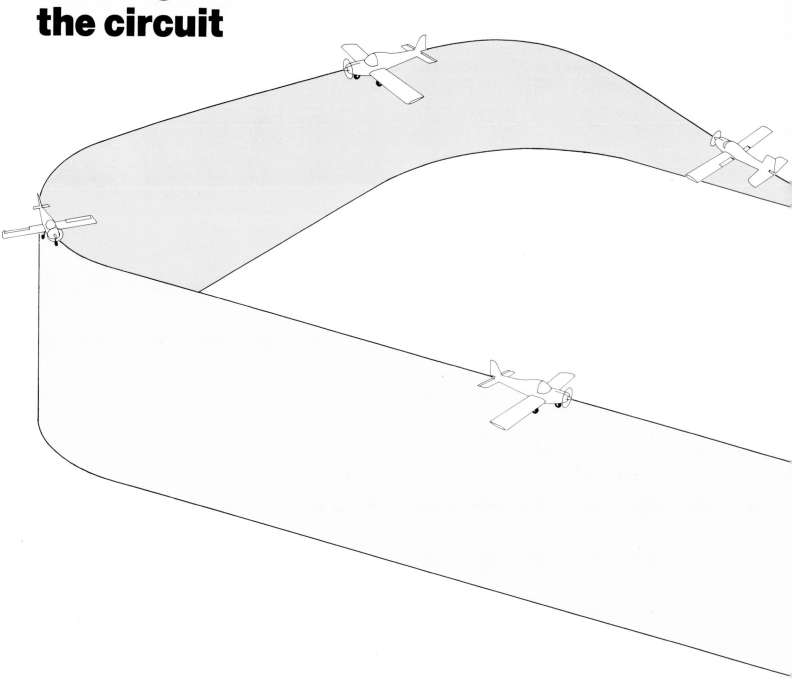

The complete circuit

The Circuit

Since early in my training the phrase 'when you come to do circuits' had been held out as a major goal. Actually arriving at this stage seemed like getting into long trousers at last.

What does it involve? The Circuit is about learning how to take off and climb away, fly round the aerodrome in the correct manner, make a proper approach to land, and finally, land again. I found it a bit like taking a lead part in some amateur theatricals, with certain cues to commit to memory, movements to get right and even a couple of small speeches, plus a monologue. (There is also, of course, an audience, although we shall probably know ourselves whether we have given an indifferent performance or a passable one).

There are some variations of the last part, the approach. We shall start by doing a so-called 'normal approach', using flap and power to adjust the descent to the runway threshold. When we have got the hang of that we shall learn, as a form of emergency training, both how to land without flap and without using power — the glide approach.

As a start Jeanne drew out a plan of the circuit on the blackboard, marking in the various things which had to be done on the way round. Some of it was familiar. Most pupils get introduced to the idea of taking off during the earlier part of the training, and I had begun some lessons previously following through on the controls and eventually taking off unaided as we set off for the training area. Similarly, I had been doing approaches to land as we came home, although I hadn't actually got as far as landing the machine unaided. The idea of circuit training is to pull all the experience together. I would carry on with it until I was proficient enough to do it solo, the next great stage in my flying training.

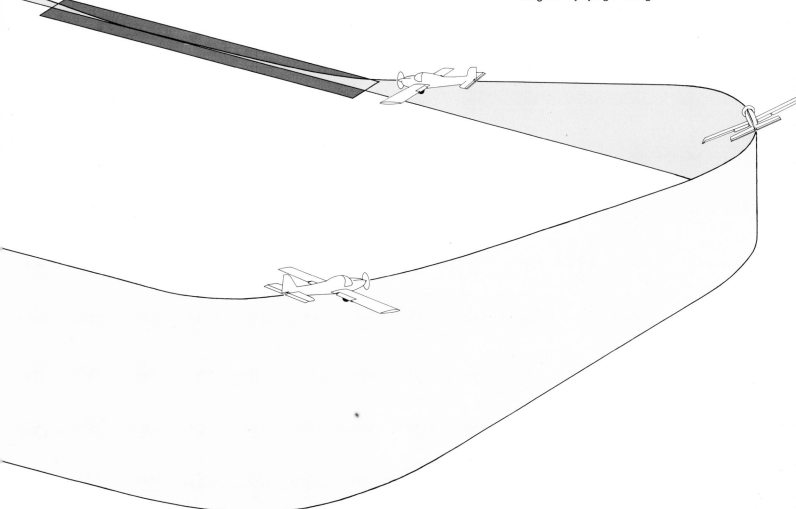

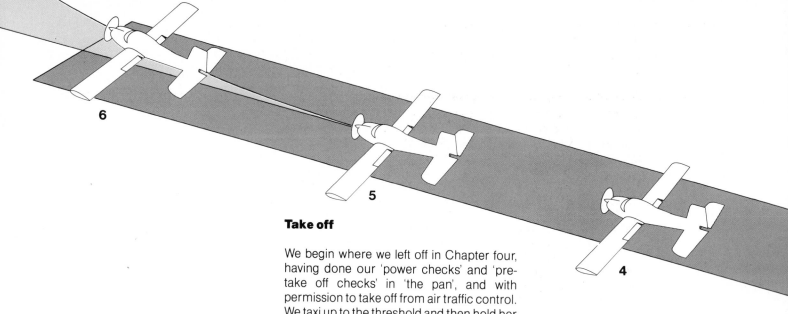

Take off

We begin where we left off in Chapter four, having done our 'power checks' and 'pre-take off checks' in 'the pan', and with permission to take off from air traffic control. We taxi up to the threshold and then hold her steady for a moment while making a last check of the engine temperatures and pressures, and looking to see that the Direction Indicator and Compass are somewhere around the heading that corresponds to the runway direction (i.e. if we are taking off from runway 27 we should expect the DI and Compass to show 270, due West. If the DI is a few degrees off, this is the time to adjust it).

1 As soon as we are ready we give her full power nice and slowly with a firm smooth shove on the throttle, fixing our eyes on the dotted white centre line running down the middle of the runway (provided we are lucky enough to be taking off from a runway which has a dotted white centre line). The important thing is to fix our eyes on *something* straight ahead, even if it is only a church steeple.

2 We need a point towards which to steer. As soon as we put on full power we shall feel the Cheetah trying to veer off towards the left, thanks to the effect of the slipstream vortex that we talked about in Chapter five.

3 At first the rudder alone won't be capable of stopping this swing. We have to steer on the brakes to begin with, putting on a touch of right brake to keep the nose going up the centre line. Once we have got enough speed for the rudder to bite we slip the foot off the brake and down to the rudder pedal.

I was told as a matter of detail that the rudder on the Cheetah starts working properly at 17 knots. But it is a bit much to ask of anyone that they should watch for 17 knots to come up on the Airspeed Indicator and then exchange brake for rudder. I found it possible to make the change after about three seconds of rolling, though I was usually far too busy to notice whether we happened to be doing 17 knots at the time. The general rule is the earlier you can get on to the rudder the better. Having to make perpetual dabs on the brake doesn't assist the acceleration and doesn't do the brake much good, either.

4 She will begin to build up speed quite rapidly. As always we have to cosset the nosewheel. Holding the stick just slightly back from the middle 'neutral' position will help keep some of the weight off the front end. (It will also help avoid an unfortunate condition, to say the least, called 'wheelbarrowing', about which more in a minute).

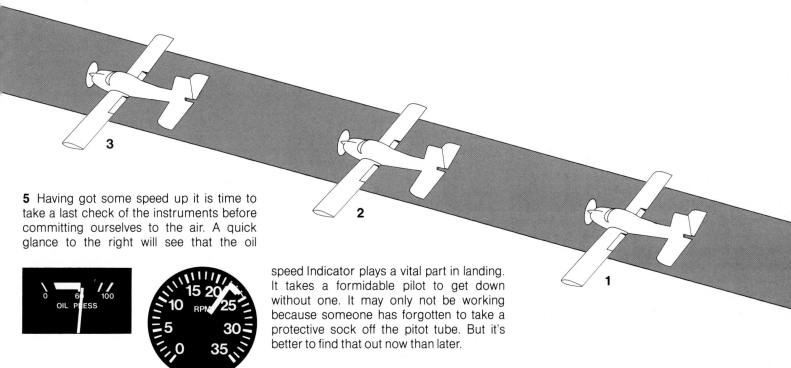

5 Having got some speed up it is time to take a last check of the instruments before committing ourselves to the air. A quick glance to the right will see that the oil

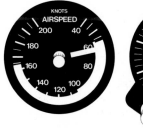

pressure is all right, and that the engine revs are keeping up around the 2200 mark. (That is what we expect from this engine at full power when it is given the task of dragging the aeroplane along the ground from a standstill). We must also check that the Airspeed Indicator is working. If it obviously isn't, it is time to change our plans and abort the take-off by closing the throttle and hauling the control column right back so that the elevators will help the slowing down process by producing some drag. We shall also probably need to tread on the brakes. Why not take off even though the Airspeed Indicator isn't working? Because the Air-

speed Indicator plays a vital part in landing. It takes a formidable pilot to get down without one. It may only not be working because someone has forgotten to take a protective sock off the pitot tube. But it's better to find that out now than later.

6 When she arrives at 65 knots we can leave the ground. All that is needed is a little bit more back pressure on the control column, and away she'll go. (What happens, in fact, is that by raising the nose a fraction we increase the angle of attack of the wings, which provides just enough extra lift to get us going up into the air).

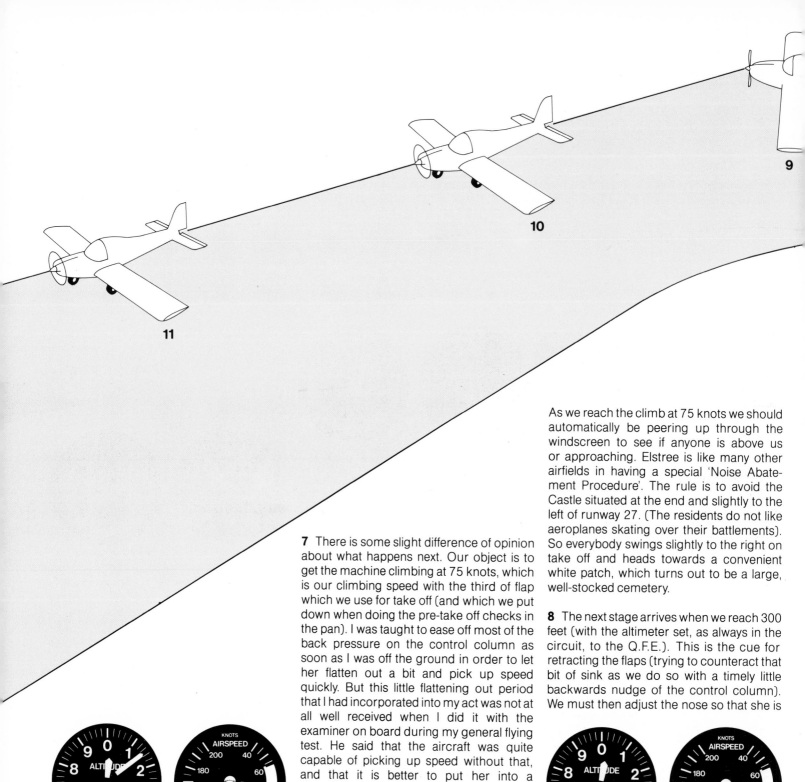

7 There is some slight difference of opinion about what happens next. Our object is to get the machine climbing at 75 knots, which is our climbing speed with the third of flap which we use for take off (and which we put down when doing the pre-take off checks in the pan). I was taught to ease off most of the back pressure on the control column as soon as I was off the ground in order to let her flatten out a bit and pick up speed quickly. But this little flattening out period that I had incorporated into my act was not at all well received when I did it with the examiner on board during my general flying test. He said that the aircraft was quite capable of picking up speed without that, and that it is better to put her into a gentle climb right from the start, gaining height as quickly as we can. As a result I nowadays practise a blend of both, not exactly flattening out, but not holding her to too much of an early climb either!

As we reach the climb at 75 knots we should automatically be peering up through the windscreen to see if anyone is above us or approaching. Elstree is like many other airfields in having a special 'Noise Abatement Procedure'. The rule is to avoid the Castle situated at the end and slightly to the left of runway 27. (The residents do not like aeroplanes skating over their battlements). So everybody swings slightly to the right on take off and heads towards a convenient white patch, which turns out to be a large, well-stocked cemetery.

8 The next stage arrives when we reach 300 feet (with the altimeter set, as always in the circuit, to the Q.F.E.). This is the cue for retracting the flaps (trying to counteract that bit of sink as we do so with a timely little backwards nudge of the control column). We must then adjust the nose so that she is

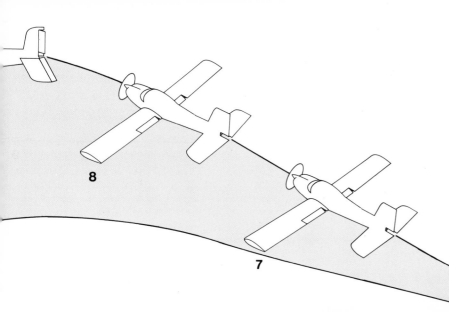

8

7

climbing a bit faster, at 85 knots. Having settled down at that speed (making sure that she is properly balanced with our famous ball in the middle) we trim off any pressure from the control column and let her carry on climbing by herself.

The Crosswind Leg

9 When 500 feet comes up on the Altimeter we begin the first turn of the circuit. When Air Traffic Control gave us the 'Circuit Information' we will have been told whether it is a right or left hand circuit. For the purpose of the diagram we have assumed a left hand circuit, which means that the first gentle turn is to the left. After a good look out what is needed is a modest 15 degrees of bank which will take us round on a course at right angles to the runway. (It is a gentle bank, because as we noted in Chapter eight 'Climbing', a steep bank sacrifices lift and would therefore undermine our climb. Getting up as rapidly as possible to our circuit height of 1000 feet is the main priority at the moment).

10 As we come round a look over the left shoulder will, or should, reveal the runway. It is a good idea to judge when we are at the required right angle to the runway by sight (it happens when the wings and the runway are roughly parallel). But the Direction Indicator is also there to help us. If the runway is facing due west at 270 degrees, then we will obviously need to be flying at around 180 degrees, due south, for this part of the circuit. Once we have got there we are on what is called 'the Cross Wind Leg'. (The circuit is divided into three 'legs', crosswind, downwind and base).

If there is a strong wind it is, of course, no use pointing the aeroplane at right angles to the runway and hoping that she will proceed in that direction. The wind will drift her to the left, which will make for an untidy circuit, cutting off the corner and making the whole circuit shape look squashed and irregular. So when the wind is strong and the aeroplane seems to be moving crab-wise across the ground, the nose needs to be pointed just a few degrees into the wind to keep the ideal rectangular pattern.

11 The aircraft is still climbing up on the crosswind leg towards the circuit height of 1000 feet. When we get there it's time to level off with the usual Attitude-Power-Trim routine, and carry on with our 100 knot cruise, keeping a special look out over to the right for other aircraft. As we shall later learn, there are various accepted ways of arriving at an aerodrome from elsewhere and joining the circuit ready for a landing. One of them is to join in on the downwind leg, which can be awkward if there is already an aeroplane in the circuit about to turn onto the downwind leg itself. Although joining aircraft are supposed to give way to aeroplanes already in the circuit, that presupposes an ideal world. The fact that we can see him doesn't mean that he has seen us. So we need to keep a good lookout for anyone else arriving to join the merry-go-round.

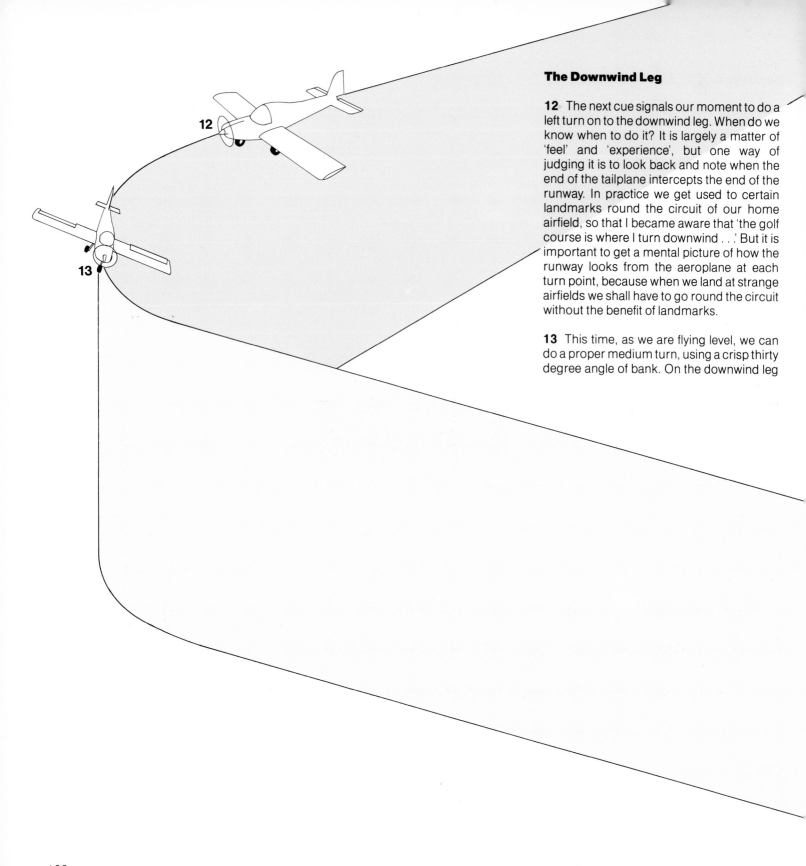

The Downwind Leg

12 The next cue signals our moment to do a left turn on to the downwind leg. When do we know when to do it? It is largely a matter of 'feel' and 'experience', but one way of judging it is to look back and note when the end of the tailplane intercepts the end of the runway. In practice we get used to certain landmarks round the circuit of our home airfield, so that I became aware that 'the golf course is where I turn downwind . . .' But it is important to get a mental picture of how the runway looks from the aeroplane at each turn point, because when we land at strange airfields we shall have to go round the circuit without the benefit of landmarks.

13 This time, as we are flying level, we can do a proper medium turn, using a crisp thirty degree angle of bank. On the downwind leg we fly parallel to the runway. Looking over to the left it will be easy to judge whether we are being blown closer in or further out by wind, and we can make a slight heading alteration accordingly.

14 The next cue comes when we arrive abreast of the end of the runway, the so-called 'upwind' end. This is where we tell air traffic control where we have got to, by calling 'Downwind'. All it involves is a curt message on the lines of: 'Bravo Mike, Downwind'. Hopefully the controller will thereupon acknowledge with something like: 'Bravo Mike, call Finals'. This simply tells us that he wants us to call him again when we are settled into our final approach, the last act of this little drama. He may also add something about: 'You are number three', which means that there are two aircraft ahead in the circuit. We may, or may not, have been aware of this cheerful fact. If we can see them up ahead we can be highly efficient and acknowledge his bit of information with: 'Roger, number three, have contact two ahead'. If we can't see them we just acknowledge that we are 'number three', and have a good look for them. It will then be appreciated just how difficult it is to

spot aeroplanes that are against a background of *terra firma* on their approach to land, so a good look out must be kept.

It may be that he will be busy talking to someone else when we reach the point abreast of the end of the runway. In that case we just wait until he has finished, and perhaps call 'late downwind', to inform him that we are well on the way round.

Having called 'downwind' (or before calling it if the controller is busy) the time has come for our short monologue, entitled 'the downwind checks'. At Elstree we called them 'the FFAB checks', i.e.

15 F fuel, that we are switched to the fullest tank, that the electric fuel pump is on, and that the mixture knob is pressed right home to 'rich'.

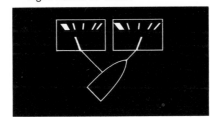

16 F flap, that they are fully up (though later, when doing instrument approaches, this is the point when we put two thirds of flap down).

17 A altimeter, check that we are at 1000 feet, and that it is set to the aerodrome Q.F.E. (which it will be, provided that we haven't moved it since setting it there before take off).

18 B brakes, make sure that they are off, by seeing that the parking brake knob is pushed in and giving a quick dab on the brake pedals with the feet.

Having done all this we shall continue keeping a good look out, taking care to look away from the airfield towards the outside of the circuit, which is where any stray joining aircraft will be coming from. With the wind behind us on this downwind leg we shall probably find ourselves passing over the ground at some speed, so we must be ready for the next cue when it comes. (Spare moments can be used to do anything useful, like giving the engine a spell of carburettor heat to make sure we haven't picked up any icing, checking the engine temperatures and pressures).

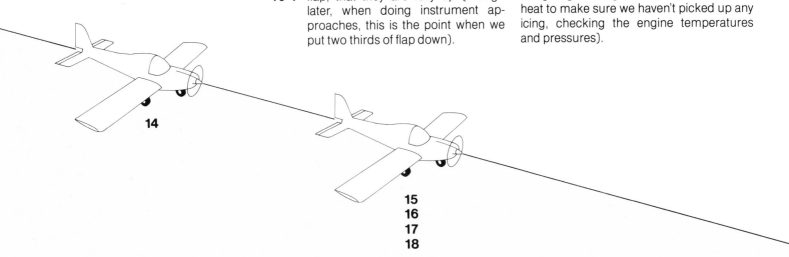

14

15
16
17
18

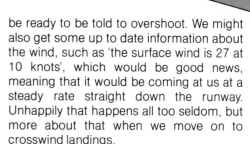

28

The Base Leg

19 The moment for turning (another normal medium turn) on to Base Leg comes when we see the runway threshold at an angle of about forty-five degrees from our side view. We should see it sitting there, midway between the back of the wing and the tailplane. Don't forget to look out before the turn. As with the crosswind leg, it may be necessary to point the nose slightly into the wind to make sure we aren't going to be swept away from the airfield.

20 Now it's time to begin preparing the aircraft for landing. We have done descending already in previous lessons. This is the real thing. Closing the throttle, we keep the nose up a moment to let the speed come back to well within the white arc on the airspeed indicator (flap operating range), lower two thirds of flap and gently push forward on the control column to lower the nose at the same time. Having done that we edge the throttle forward to feed on a little bit of power, around 1600 to 1700 revs will do to start with, though we shall probably have to change it on the way down according to whether we seem to be too high or too low.

21 The speed we want at this stage is 80 knots, and having got that by adjusting the nose attitude, we trim her and let her come down on her own. We can then spend our time peering out to the right to see that no one is coming in unheralded on a long 'straight in' approach to the runway, and peering out to the left to see how we are getting on towards the point where we have to turn in to the runway on 'Finals'.

22 The aim is to end up facing straight down the runway on what is called 'the centre line', a line extended into space which corresponds to the white line down the middle of the runway. It is obviously no use waiting until we are on the centre line before turning. We shall end up too far to the right of where we want to be. So we start the turn just short of where we estimate the centre line to be. When we make this turn on to Finals we should be at about 600 feet, provided the preceding bits have been done properly. It is not the end of the world if we are higher or lower than that. But the 600 feet figure is useful for giving some guidance about whether we are going to find ourselves coming in too high or too low on Finals.

23 The turn on to Finals should be quite gentle, not more than 15 to 20 degrees, because we are descending already and don't want to increase the rate of descent too sharply at this stage.

24 Once on Finals we need to slow the aeroplane down a bit, so it's down with the rest of the flap, together with an adjustment of the nose to get 70 knots. Having got it, we trim so that she comes down at that speed on her own, leaving us the opportunity to ponder other things.

25 This is the point to give the Finals radio call, simply: 'Bravo Mike, Finals'. The Controller will normally say 'Clear to land', but there may be variations if something is going on down there. If he (or she) says 'Bravo Mike, continue your approach' it means that someone is milling around on the runway who could obstruct a landing, so

be ready to be told to overshoot. We might also get some up to date information about the wind, such as 'the surface wind is 27 at 10 knots', which would be good news, meaning that it would be coming at us at a steady rate straight down the runway. Unhappily that happens all too seldom, but more about that when we move on to crosswind landings.

26 Our task now is to judge whether we are coming in at just the right height to end up with the machine nicely placed over the runway threshold. Getting used to the right picture is the key. If the end of the runway seems to be crawling up the windscreen we

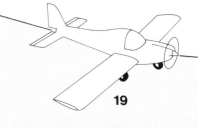

19

are too low. If it is sinking down to the bottom of the windscreen we are too high. It is, in fact, not difficult to get it right once the great secret has been learned, that HEIGHT ADJUSTMENTS ARE MADE WITH THE THROTTLE. Leave the elevators alone unless and until we want to make an adjustment of speed. Once the Cheetah was properly trimmed for 70 knots she didn't seem to need much in the way of speed correction, even when the power was adjusted. If we seemed to be coming in too low and put on more power, the nose came up automatically and the speed stayed the same. Only the rate of descent changed.

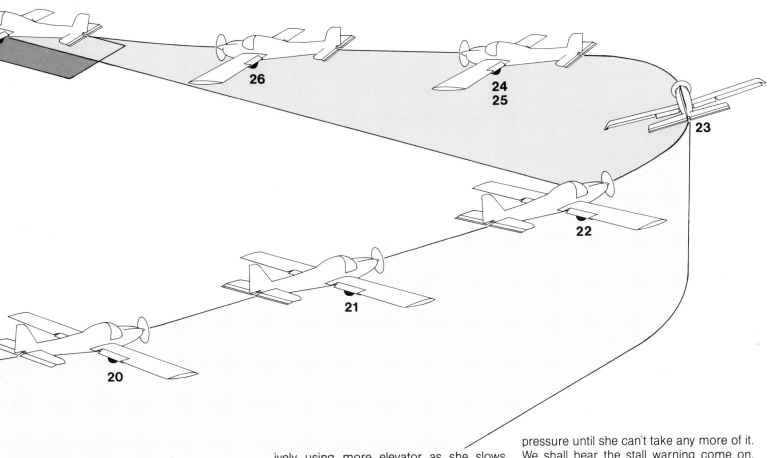

27 But 70 knots is still too fast for the landing. So just before we reach the threshold we bring the nose up slightly to slow her down to 65 knots. At this point we should be at what Jeanne called 'the height of a double-decker bus'.

28 We now do what is termed 'the round out', which simply involves a gentle backward movement of the stick over the runway threshold to check the descent and get her flying level just above the runway, simultaneously closing the throttle and getting rid of any remaining power. The idea is to keep her flying as long as possible by progress-

ively using more elevator as she slows down. About seven inches above the runway is a pretty height to do this bit! Looking straight ahead, bringing her down the white line, we just progressively bring the stick back, hold it, bring the stick back, hold it, so that we end up with the nose quite high as she simply stops flying and eases herself gently onto the ground.

This is what takes most of the time, learning how to keep her at the same height just above the runway as the speed drops off. As the speed goes, so she will want to come down, but we stop her with more back pressure. It is just a gradual increase of back

pressure until she can't take any more of it. We shall hear the stall warning come on, which on this occasion is a happy sound, because it means we are doing the job properly. She is about to give up flying and subside gently onto the ground with a gratifying 'squidge' of rubber tyres.

This is the ideal. It took me some time to reach it. There are a number of common faults and I seem to have made them all, plus one or two special ones of my own. We shall look at the practical problems in the next chapter. Nevertheless, once the landing is mastered, there are few more satisfying things in aviation than a perfect descent to the ground.

Chapter 14:
How do we get down: the landing

One thing impressed on me from the start of the landing lessons was the fact that if things don't seem to be going right it is best to forget it, abandon the touch-down, put on full power and go round again. This is probably good advice, but it adds up to an admission of defeat which it was hard for a pigheaded novice like myself to accept. As a result I persevered with some shocking landings in the early stages, which at least qualifies me to describe them.

I had rigged up a tape recorder in the intercom circuit, so I can now bring on a severe attack of humility and embarrassment merely by playing myself these early tapes. It is one of the standing rules of flying instruction that students should never be allowed to become depressed or unconfident; instructors, even in the worst patches, should always try and find something to praise. This posed a problem for Jeanne sometimes. After one particularly atrocious bump I have her on tape saying gamely: 'Well, the actual shape of the circuit itself was beautiful ...'

So: **Faults**

1 My earliest one was to round out from the descent and hold the aeroplane off the ground far too high. I saw the ground coming up fast, hauled back on the control column and brought her steadily to a standstill while still some ten feet off the ground. The result was that she fell down with a hefty bump and bounced up into the air again. I would do this, hanging on to the control column, in spite of the fact that the advice to 'Let her come down, let her come down ...' was being fed into my ears. The way to avoid this unseemly bounce down the runway is to be ready with a bit of power in order to ease her down gently, which is why it is essential always to have one hand on the throttle during the landing, because you never know when you are going to need it.

2 A disastrous habit crept into my way of handling the control column. Instead of a steady backwards ... hold it ... backwards ... hold it ... backwards ... and so on, gradually bringing the stick further and further towards me in a regular progression, I indulged in a twitchy backwards ... forwards ... backwards ... forwards ... routine. I suspect this was a hangover from some dimly remembered competition car driving technique. It left the poor aeroplane without any clear idea of what was expected of it, with the usual result that it met the ground before it had properly finished flying and promptly took off again.

3 As some kind of reaction to Fault 1 I found myself falling into the opposite error, not holding off enough, trying to complete the grisly business of getting on the ground too early. But if I pointed her to the ground when there were still 65-70 knots on the Airspeed Indicator she would obviously take off into the air again, because that was still a respect-

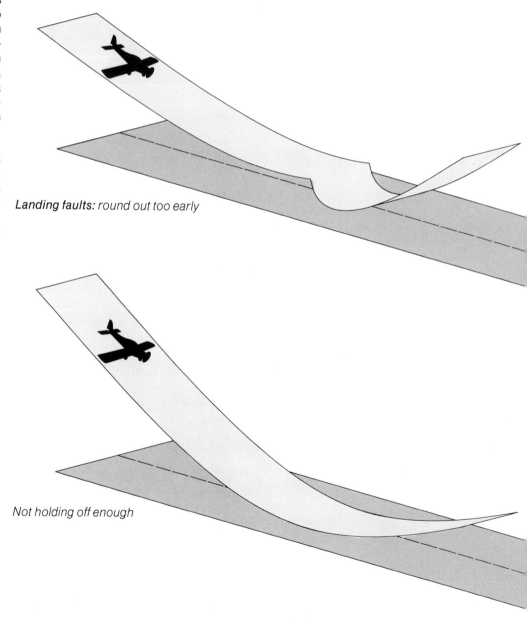

Landing faults: round out too early

Not holding off enough

able flying speed. Pushing the stick forward and trying to hold her on the runway is no way to try to overcome this problem, because it is the prelude to a bent nosewheel. She has got to come down when she is ready to come down. Usually I only did small bumps on these occasions and by gently keeping her flying and letting her down gradually with the proper backward stick movements I would get her down smoothly in the end. But if it is a big bump and she goes up like a balloon I was advised to put on full power and take her away.

4 I then found myself paying so much attention to getting the height of the round-out right that I didn't pay enough attention to my speed on the final approach. The result of that was that I arrived at the runway threshold too fast, so that my little backward nudges were enough to make her actually gain height again, which caused all sorts of problems. I would still be trying to fight the aeroplane down to the ground about half way up the runway, which is not good. 'Good landings are made up there', I was told by Jeanne, as she pointed towards the bit of sky used on the final approach.

5 Then there were the times when, intent on getting speed and height right, I let the direction go to pot and landed on the side of the runway instead of in the middle. 'Don't be afraid to turn on the final approach to get yourself properly positioned', I was told. I found myself having to overcome a positive disinclination to doing this in the final moments, as though the actual portion of runway used for the landing was somehow pre-ordained. What does it matter, as long as we end up on the hard bit? Because numbers of things, including a burst tyre or an unexpected side gust, can swing the aircraft to one side on landing. In such a case the more width of runway there is to play with each side of the aircraft, the better.

6 Nor were my problems confined to landing. On one take off I had the stick too far forward during the speed build-up on the ground which finally resulted in the mainwheels lifting an inch or two off the ground while the nose wheel was still in contact with the runway, the dreaded 'wheel-barrow effect!' There was a slight wind from one side at the time, with the awesome result that the whole aeroplane pivoted round to port on its nosewheel while still in the middle of the take off.

7 Nor was the shape of the circuit itself always so 'beautiful'. I had a tendency to edge in towards the airfield on the downwind leg, which I believe is common. It followed that the base leg business of preparing the aeroplane for the landing had to be carried out in rushed and cramped conditions and usually meant that I found myself turning on to 'Finals' with too much height.

Reciting all these problems may give the impression that landing is more difficult than it really is. But in between the rubbish I found myself occasionally pulling off what the trade calls 'a greaser', the ideal article. For me the breakthrough came when I got the right feel of holding the control column firmly and steadily, with no jerky, nervous movements, using it to hold the aeroplane up off the ground for as long as possible, until Nature takes over and lowers her gently to the ground. It's a lovely feeling when you get it right.

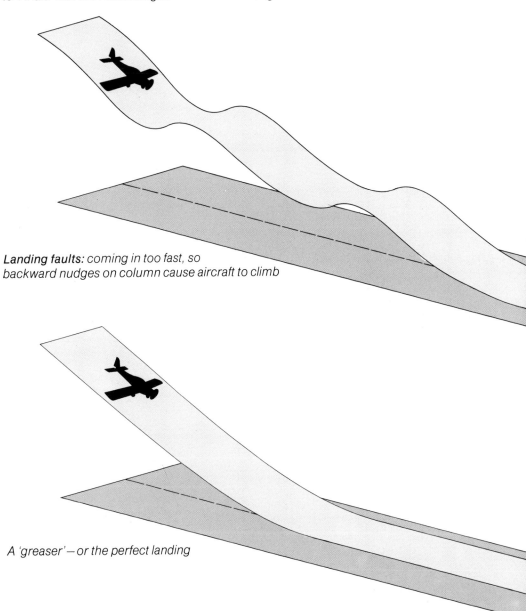

Landing faults: coming in too fast, so backward nudges on column cause aircraft to climb

A 'greaser' — or the perfect landing

Choose base area of
1000ft, glide at 80kts,
carburettor heat on

The glide approach to landing

1 *Calm conditions*
2 *Medium conditions*
3 *Strong wind blowing down runway*

Chapter 15:
The gliding approach – softly, softly

Having spent three sessions on 'normal' approaches it was time to move onto something harder, the glide approach. The object is to get the aeroplane down neatly without the comforting help of the throttle. This obviously means that we have got to be clever about judging the height on the approach to the runway. There are various ways of losing height if we have too much of it. But for this exercise there will be no way of gaining any height if we find ourselves coming in too low.

Knowing how to judge it correctly is the same skill that is needed for a successful forced landing after an engine failure. For this reason much time is spent teaching people to get it right. It could save their lives. As usual, it began with a drawing on the briefing room blackboard.

We start by coming in on the downwind leg just as for the normal approach. But just before turning on to base leg we choose a point on the ground known as the 'Thousand Foot Area' (also sometimes known as the 'Base Area'). The choice of this spot (which can be anything that stands out as a landmark, like a group of trees, a cabbage patch or a building) is the key to the whole business. For this is the point over which we shall shut off the engine in the confident hope that we will be able to glide in safely to a perfect landing on the runway.

In practising round the aerodrome I found myself gradually getting it right and picking the perfect spot for whichever runway was in use. Then I would try again a few days later and find that I was falling too short, and was forced to use an ignominious burst of power to avoid coming down in the trees in front of the runway. In this way it was brought home to me that every day is different for glide approaches. We are creatures of the wind. If there is a strong wind blowing straight down the runway it will obviously be important to choose a 'Thousand Foot Area' that is further in than the one we might have chosen on a calm day. (The various ways that wind affects the choice of 'Thousand Foot Area' are shown as numbers in the drawing). Different types of aircraft also have different gliding capabilities, which is why it is important to be

thoroughly checked out before flying off in an unfamiliar aeroplane.

Doing glide approaches as part of circuit training is a great deal easier than being forced to do an accurate glide approach to an unfamiliar field if the engine stops during a cross country. But the principle is the same. We get the aircraft into a steady glide at 80 knots, pick a turning point, taking the wind speed and direction into consideration, and aim to be at a height of one thousand feet above it, bearing in mind that if we are too low there is nothing we will be able to do about it.

For this reason it is usual to aim for too much height, rather than trying to judge it exactly from the start. Height can always be disposed of. The run in can be lengthened, by turning in or out on the base leg. Putting down flap will also hasten the descent, although the rule is 'Only One Third At A Time'. At each stage of flap we need to convince ourselves that we have plenty of height in hand before putting down the next stage. I found myself asking the question, with my finger on the flap switch: 'Am I really going to make it? Yes, right, next stage of flap.'

So we close the throttle when we think we can make the airfield, the exact point depending on wind strength, (having taken the

When aircraft is trimmed check height. If too low cut corner of base leg, if too high carry on then cut back. If height is OK put one third flap on just before the turn

In an ideal world we should then find ourselves with enough height to put down the second third of flap and bring the speed back to 75 knots. Still got plenty of height? Then let's put all the flap down, which will give us a really steep descent at 70 knots for the last part. The technique of actually getting the plane on the ground was slightly different when using no power at all, I discovered. We seemed to be coming down at a much steeper angle, with a lower nose and a much more rapid approach to the ground. This meant that a bit more levelling out was needed to get the machine gliding above the runway, preparing for the touch down. For this reason I was advised to start the round-out a bit earlier than normal as there was more 'rounding out' to be done.

Height still OK, two thirds flap, speed back to 75kts

Still OK, full flap, steep descent of 70kts

One other refinement was brought to my notice. As we are merely gliding along as a creature of the elements, the aircraft is much more responsive to changes of wind strength or direction than when power is being used. There is an area close to the ground where wind strength can, on occasions, drop off considerably, due to the effect of objects on the ground sticking up into the breeze and slowing it down (though the flat expanses of airfields are windier places than most). This 'wind gradient' needs watching out for. An aircraft meeting a sudden calm is effectively suddenly deprived of a slice of its flying speed. So we need to watch the airspeed in the latter stages and stick the nose down if we see it suddenly drop. This is called 'lowering the nose into the wind gradient'.

I was kept at these glide approaches on days of varying winds until I could get them right without having to scramble in by a hair's breadth. For the sake of practice I was even made to include what are called the Crash Checks on the final approach, a routine which is normally gone through before making a forced landing. This involved simulating the precautions which will help us get out of the aeroplane safely in the event of a sharp, abrupt arrival: unlatching the canopy (so that it will be possible to open it even if the body is slightly distorted), straps tight, fuel off, magnetos off, electrics off, and finally the Master Switch and Alternator Switch off (but not, of course, for real).

precaution of pulling the carburettor heat out) and let the speed come back to 80 knots before lowering the nose and trimming her for a glide in the normal way. Having sorted her out it is time to size up the situation and see how we are getting on. A bit on the low side? If so, it might be advisable to abandon the Base Leg early, cut off the corner and head straight for the runway (see illustration). Or are we too high? We can edge out on the base leg and so extend the final approach.

For these glide approaches I was told always to aim to touch down well into the runway, as much as a third of the way down. This not only gives us a bit of height margin to play with, it is also good forced landing practice. For the wisdom of the ages dictates that it is better to misjudge things slightly and contact the far hedge of a field at a comparatively slow speed than to misjudge things and contact the near hedge at flying speed. If we think we have height in hand a third of flap put down just before turning the corner onto Finals was recommended, but I usually waited until I was actually facing the runway on the Final Approach before committing myself to anything.

As descent is steeper than usual, round off earlier. Watch out for wind near ground

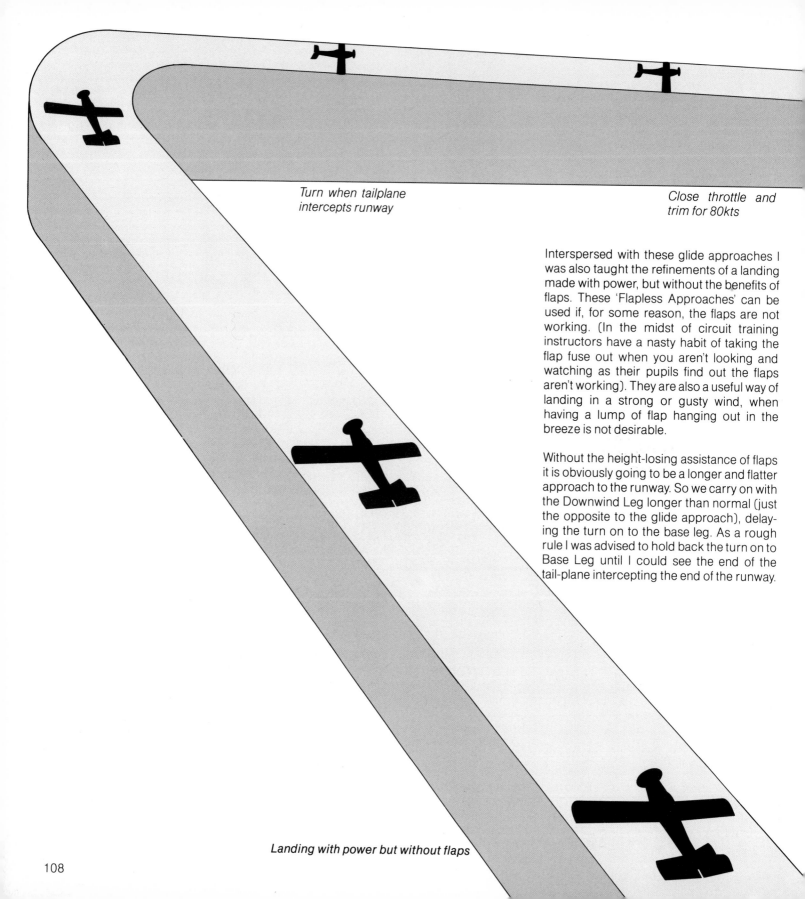

Turn when tailplane intercepts runway

Close throttle and trim for 80kts

Interspersed with these glide approaches I was also taught the refinements of a landing made with power, but without the benefits of flaps. These 'Flapless Approaches' can be used if, for some reason, the flaps are not working. (In the midst of circuit training instructors have a nasty habit of taking the flap fuse out when you aren't looking and watching as their pupils find out the flaps aren't working). They are also a useful way of landing in a strong or gusty wind, when having a lump of flap hanging out in the breeze is not desirable.

Without the height-losing assistance of flaps it is obviously going to be a longer and flatter approach to the runway. So we carry on with the Downwind Leg longer than normal (just the opposite to the glide approach), delaying the turn on to the base leg. As a rough rule I was advised to hold back the turn on to Base Leg until I could see the end of the tail-plane intercepting the end of the runway.

Landing with power but without flaps

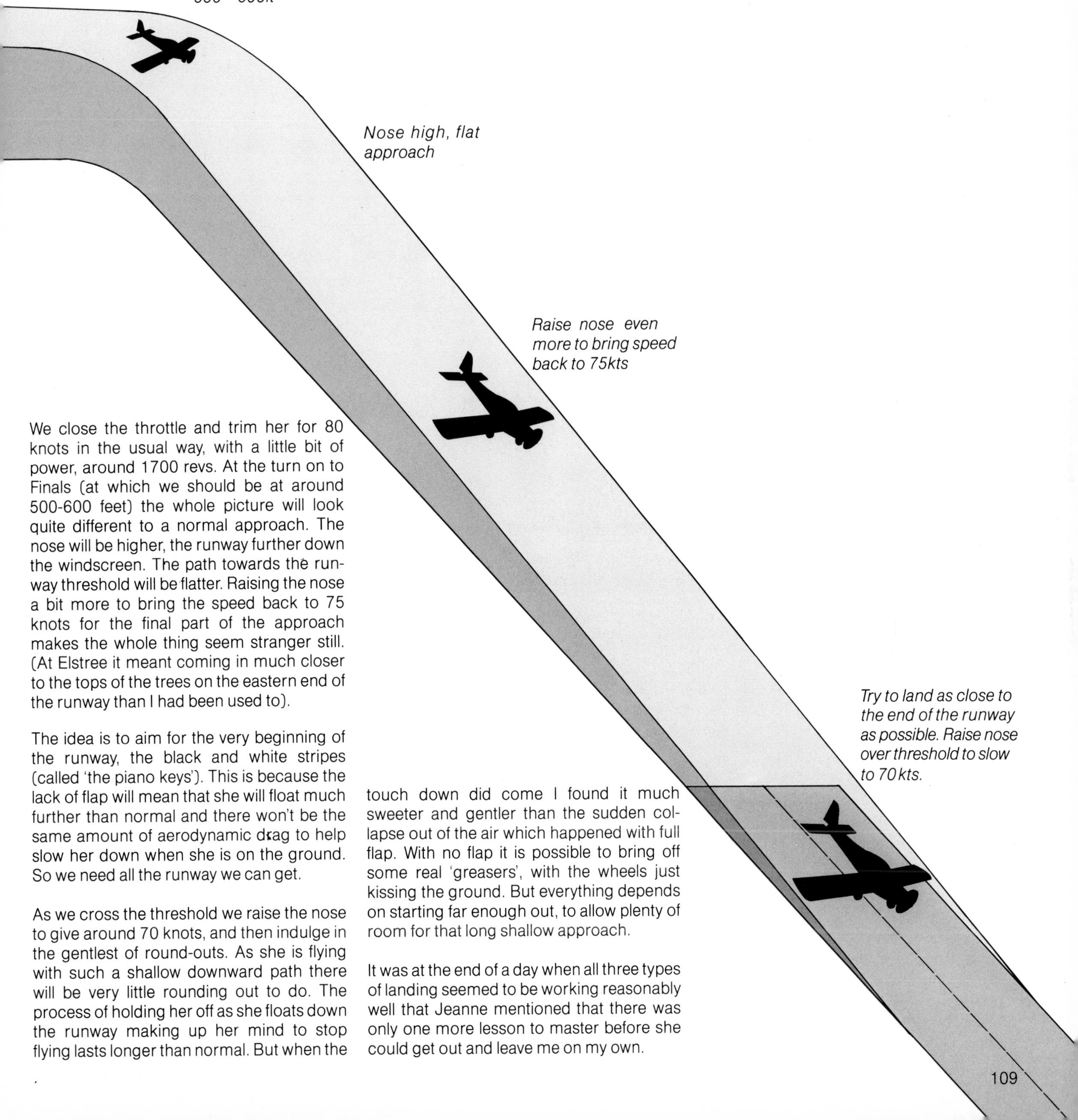

*Turn into finals at
500–600ft*

*Nose high, flat
approach*

*Raise nose even
more to bring speed
back to 75kts*

*Try to land as close to
the end of the runway
as possible. Raise nose
over threshold to slow
to 70kts.*

We close the throttle and trim her for 80 knots in the usual way, with a little bit of power, around 1700 revs. At the turn on to Finals (at which we should be at around 500-600 feet) the whole picture will look quite different to a normal approach. The nose will be higher, the runway further down the windscreen. The path towards the runway threshold will be flatter. Raising the nose a bit more to bring the speed back to 75 knots for the final part of the approach makes the whole thing seem stranger still. (At Elstree it meant coming in much closer to the tops of the trees on the eastern end of the runway than I had been used to).

The idea is to aim for the very beginning of the runway, the black and white stripes (called 'the piano keys'). This is because the lack of flap will mean that she will float much further than normal and there won't be the same amount of aerodynamic drag to help slow her down when she is on the ground. So we need all the runway we can get.

As we cross the threshold we raise the nose to give around 70 knots, and then indulge in the gentlest of round-outs. As she is flying with such a shallow downward path there will be very little rounding out to do. The process of holding her off as she floats down the runway making up her mind to stop flying lasts longer than normal. But when the

touch down did come I found it much sweeter and gentler than the sudden collapse out of the air which happened with full flap. With no flap it is possible to bring off some real 'greasers', with the wheels just kissing the ground. But everything depends on starting far enough out, to allow plenty of room for that long shallow approach.

It was at the end of a day when all three types of landing seemed to be working reasonably well that Jeanne mentioned that there was only one more lesson to master before she could get out and leave me on my own.

Chapter 16:
Aerial calamities: engine failure after take-off

Engine failure

It would be cruel luck to get an engine failure just after take off on the first solo. But in the belief that it is vital to be prepared for anything when committing ourselves to the air I was made to practise several engine failures after take off before being left on my own to fly solo.

There are several ways of practising it. On an airfield with a long runway it is possible (having alerted the controller to what is going on) to take off at one end, climb a hundred feet, close the throttle and get down again before the rest of the runway is exhausted and the 'plane runs off the end.

But Elstree's runway is too short for that. On the day chosen for this exercise no other nearby airfield with a long runway seemed to want us, so we had to resort to another way of doing it.

This consisted of making an approach to land at Elstree that was normal in everything but the fact that it was aimed at a point about a mile or a mile and a half short of the runway. When about 200 feet from the ground, and with one third of flap on, we'd push on full power and climb away, for all the world as though we had just taken off. At the crucial moment, out comes the throttle and off goes the power. It was then my job to get her down safely onto the runway which happened to appear, so conveniently, under the nose. This is a fairly tame and far from ideal way of simulating the real thing. For one thing, it misses out the grim necessity of making a rapid choice of somewhere to land. But it teaches the two basic rules, which we discussed before going off to try it.

Rule One: Never, NEVER, try to turn back towards the airfield you have just departed from. It is a trap which has caused the demise of many pilots. The laws of nature decree that the height lost in a gliding 180 degree turn makes it impossible. What usually happens to people who try it is that they hold the nose up, desperately trying to stretch the glide. The inevitable result is a stall and spin, with no time to recover.

I have always been prepared to accept this rule as being common sense. But for anyone who wants to be totally, scientifically convinced, I recommend a set of calculations that I came across in Alan Bramson's *Be A Better Pilot* (Martin Dunitz). There is something about the chilling inevitability of the cold mathematics set down there which makes turning back to the airfield after an engine failure on take off seem as pointless as jumping out of a ten-storey window.

The correct way is to select a landing spot straight ahead, or within 30 degrees of the take off path if that isn't possible. If there really is nowhere in that direction, then it is just permissible to turn as much as sixty degrees from the take off path if you have enough height, but no more than that.

None of this will be any good, however, unless we observe Rule Two: Get the nose down straight away. If the engine stops during a climb the aeroplane will lose flying

110

speed and stall almost immediately unless we are very quick with a forward movement of the control column. If it happens in the climb out below 300 feet we shall be likely to have the one third of flap we used for the take off. We are stuck with it. Don't try and get it up, I was warned, because the aircraft will sink and go down even further in the process. So what we are looking for is a straightforward 70 knot glide to a convenient set of empty rugby pitches, open fields or whatever a benevolent Providence has laid out in

our path. Above 300 feet, with the flaps up, we glide ahead at 75 knots. The higher we are when it happens the better, of course. On the way down we get through as many pre-crash checks as there is time for.

It was stressed to me quite vigorously that these engine failures on take off (or EFATOs) do not in the normal course of events happen with modern, reliable and well maintained aero engines. Nevertheless, it is as well to be prepared, as was demonstrated by an incident which happened to a novice pilot with under fifty hours at another airfield (not Elstree) just before I began my course. His engine stopped at 400 feet, but following his recently learned drill he got the machine safely down, having switched all the switches off, given out an emergency Mayday call on the radio and calmly gone through every one of the pre-crash checks.

Having heard about this I found it judicious to look out for likely spots at each end of the Elstree runway, just in case I might need them one day.

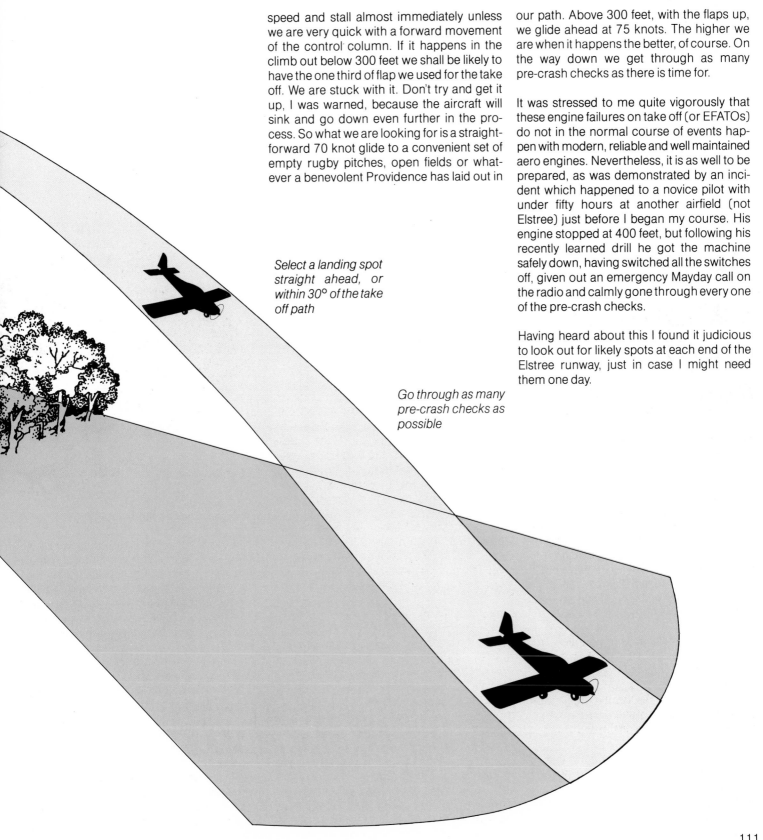

Select a landing spot straight ahead, or within 30° of the take off path

Go through as many pre-crash checks as possible

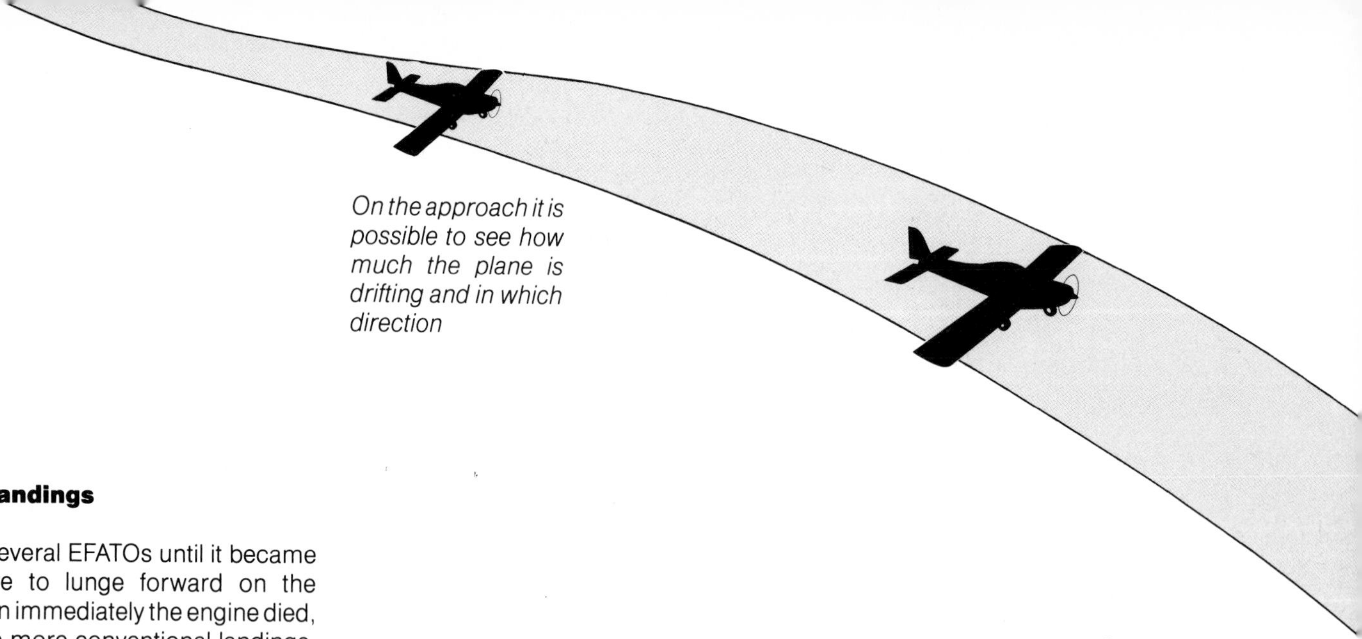

On the approach it is possible to see how much the plane is drifting and in which direction

Crosswind landings

Crosswind landings

Having tried several EFATOs until it became second nature to lunge forward on the control column immediately the engine died, we tried some more conventional landings, with the difference that the wind was blowing slightly across the runway, rather than straight down it. This was to be my initiation into crosswind landings, a skill which I found quite difficult to master.

The problem is that when the airflow is moving slightly across the runway an aeroplane coming in for a landing will also be moving slightly sideways. Unless something is done about it there will be a nasty sideways lurch and skid on touch-down, which is not good for the undercarriage.

There are two recognised methods of dealing with this problem, but I was taught only one of them, the so-called 'crabbing' method.

As we make the approach to land it is possible to see how much the aircraft is drifting to one side. It is then a fairly simple matter to turn the nose slightly towards the direction of the wind, away from the direction of the drift. The result ideally is a crab-like final approach, which has the aircraft flying on a straight track down the centre line although the nose will actually be pointing to one side. So far, so good. But it is obviously going to be no good touching the ground in this crooked fashion, because the aircraft may then run off to one side of the runway and end up on the grass. The trick is to straighten out with a timely dab of rudder just as the wheels are about to touch down. (By now it should come as second nature to

give just a suspicion of opposite aileron as we use the rudder to straighten out, to stop the roll which follows from the 'secondary effect' of yawing the aircraft round). The accompanying drawing sets out this procedure, but what I found difficult was judging just exactly when to straighten out. If I did it too early the aircraft had time to start drifting sideways across the runway before touching down. Too late and on contact with the concrete before having got completely out of the crab position the aircraft would threaten to depart from the runway centreline and end up on the rough grass.

I found it took most of my attention to judge just how much drift there was in order to keep the aircraft on a straight track. As a result the business of holding off until the aircraft was ready to stop flying went to pot. But, like most things in flying, it came with practice. I found it helped to forget about the fact that I was approaching in a strange sideways manner and just concentrate on the landing requirements until the last minute. With time it became possible to judge just when she was about to give up flying. That was the moment to weigh in with the rudder.

The problems were not completely over once on the ground. I found the machine tending to veer over into the direction of the wind (caused by the airflow striking the fin). The rudder alone was not always enough to keep her rolling straight. A dab of brake was sometimes needed.

These crosswind difficulties are a reminder that even in a powerful aeroplane we are playthings of our element, just as a ship is at the mercy of currents and tides. I ended up more or less able to deal with a cross wind, but I was thankful that on the day of my next big step, the first solo, the wind was obligingly blowing straight down the runway and quite gently at that.

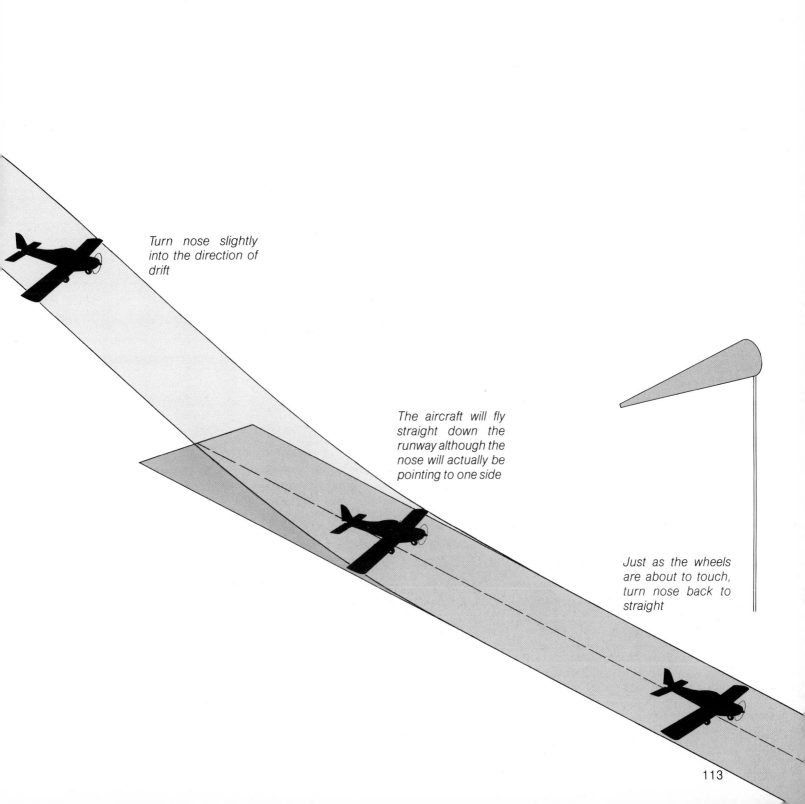

Turn nose slightly into the direction of drift

The aircraft will fly straight down the runway although the nose will actually be pointing to one side

Just as the wheels are about to touch, turn nose back to straight

113

Chapter 17:
The great moment: the first solo

The first solo

The first solo, I was told, is 'a never-to-be-forgotten experience'. It's true. I can remember every minute of it. And just to make sure that it becomes a part of my permanent mental archive I have a scratchy tape of it. Barely audible above the engine noise can be heard my mumbled words of self-reassurance.

Some people, I believe, are taken by surprise when the instructor gets out, folds the straps neatly on the seat and walks off across the grass with a cheery farewell. But in my case I was prepared. We had talked about this being 'the solo day' if all went well. We did three circuits and a practice engine failure on take off, and I managed to get her down without any struggling on each occasion. So I was more than happy, and probably a bit over-confident, when Jeanne said: 'OK. Let's pull over on the grass and I'll get out'.

I got the lecture about it just being a normal circuit, but that if there was any doubt about the landing at all I was to throw it away and go round again. Much better to have another go and finish with a good one than make a mess of the first. As if I was going to make a mess of anything!

She made a mysterious numerical code call to the controller on the radio, which I later discovered was letting him know that he was about to have a nervous debutante on his hands going round for the first time, who needed to be treated gently. Then she got out, leaving me with gradually fading words of encouragement and farewell: 'GOODBYE, PEARSON . . . I AM SURE YOU ARE GOING TO BE FINE . . . GOODBYE . . . Goodbye . . . goodbye . . . g o o d b y e e e . . .'. I suspect it might have been more of a nerve-wracking occasion for her than it was for me.

Well. There I was, with this empty space beside me. It reminded me of the feeling of being left in the house alone as a child, hoping that no one was going to come and ring the doorbell.

Checklist on my knee, I ran through the pre-take off procedure. 'Throttle friction nut is tight . . . Mixture is rich . . . Carburettor heat is cold . . . Fuel selector, it's on and there seems to be enough for this little jaunt . . . Primer, tug, locked . . . '.

It was around here that I made my first mistake. Looking back I suppose I was thinking about what it felt like to be sitting there alone doing all this, rather than concentrating all of my mind on what I was in fact doing. I was luxuriating in the experience, rather than getting on with the job. So I missed something out, as we shall see later.

When I got to the end of the checks and called up on the radio I was surprised to find that a dry croak came out of my mouth, rather than the laid-back, laconic tone I was aiming for.

'FOXTROT GOLF, (Gulp), R-READY FOR TAKE OFF'. 'FOX GOLF, – LINE UP . . . AND HOLD'. 'FOXTRIT GOLF' (sic).

While bumping across the grass on the way to the end of the runway another gurgle came over the headset which I was not quick enough to catch, but which I guessed was giving me permission to take off after the departing Cessna, which I could see was just starting its roll. But I certainly wasn't going to go in for any 'SAY AGAIN PLEASE' at this stage. So I mumbled an acknowledgement, had a good look round to see that nothing was coming, heaved the aeroplane onto the concrete and lined her up. The Cessna was disappearing on its climb out. Was it OK for me to go now, or not? There was no one sitting beside me to ask. Good heavens, this is ridiculous. Just tell the man you are going, and go.

'FOXTROT GOLF IS ROLLING'

No answer. OK. Let's get on with it. Engine temps and pressures are good. The compass and the Direction Indicator are telling the right story. Here goes.

A firm, progressive push forward of the throttle, a touch of right brake to stop the swing, eyes on the centre line, let's try to take her right down the middle. Foot down to the rudder as the speed builds up. Now we'll see how we are getting on: temperatures and pressures still good, speed building up to around forty-five, everything seems fine.

There is a theory that the first surprise of the first solo is the way the plane lifts off much more quickly than the student expects, due to the fact that there is only one person on board. I had the control column edged well back to take the weight off the nose wheel, so as the speed built up over the fifty mark I sat expectantly waiting for that lovely feeling when the wheels stop rumbling, the plane stops shuddering and kicking, and the first signs of gentle flotation arrive. Only, it didn't. Far from staying on the ground for less time than usual, we seemed to be sticking for longer. When was the damn thing going to take off!

I had a quick look at the rev counter. Nothing wrong there. Speed up to the mid sixties now, with the nose wheel unstuck at last. Another backward nudge of the control column should have had us springing off into the atmosphere, even with two on board and full tanks. All it did for me was to haul the aeroplane with an obvious degree of unwillingness into the air, to begin a markedly shallow ascent at 75 knots. This is all very peculiar, I thought to myself, as the Elstree trees passed below, closer than usual.

The next stage was 300 feet, flaps up. I moved my finger to the switch and got ready to put some backward pressure on the control column in order to make a really professional job of counteracting the sink. There would only be me to appreciate it, but I needed the encouragement. Only, as I pushed forward on the switch, there was no sink. I looked out of the window and saw that the flaps were up. Light began to dawn. They had never been down. On the pre-take off checks I had somehow missed out 'FLAPS . . . set one third'. No wonder she had been unwilling to leap into the air. I had done a flapless take off on a calm day. Just as well I wasn't flying something big and heavy.

The psychological impact of this omission may well, on balance, have been beneficial. From then on I concentrated like fury. If my mind could let me down on a simple thing like that, what else couldn't I get wrong? Pay attention to what you are doing, man.

The next stage came along, 500 feet on the Altimeter. A gentle climbing turn to the right. No, wait a minute. Is it a right or left hand circuit? I have been doing right hand circuits all morning, but around one o'clock they usually change it. What's the time? Come on, there hasn't been a radio call about changing the circuit direction. Anyway, where did that Cessna go? Oh there he is, on the

right, and rather close. We seem to be catching him up. Naturally, with our flapless departure. OK, gentle turn right, and I think I'll widen my circuit or try and slow this thing down. I don't want to crowd in on him on the final approach. How do I go more slowly? I'll bother about that later.

As the Altimeter needle approached 1000 feet it was time to level out. It would be nice, I thought, if I could finish that manoeuvre with all the needles dead on their appropriate spots, 1000 feet, 100 knots and 180 degrees, due south. But this was where only having one on board did seem to make a difference. I was slow about the progressive forward push on the control column as the speed built up. By the time I had reached 100 knots and throttled back the Altimeter was jeering at me, showing 1200 feet. On my tape I can hear the exasperated reaction: 'GET DOWN, YOU BLIGHTER!'

Turning downwind I could see the Cessna in front, and I still seemed to be gaining. The problem now was to lose height and speed simultaneously. I brought the revs back and edged the nose up a bit at the same time. This was turning out to be a somewhat eventful and unorthodox circuit.

'FOXTROT GOLF, DOWNWIND.' It was even more of a croak.

'FOX GOLF, REPORT FINALS. NUMBER TWO.'

'FOXTROT GOLF'. For some reason I felt it would be dangerously presumptuous to indulge in any fancy shortening of my call sign 'Foxtrot' to 'Fox'. That sort of thing is best left for veterans.

The downwind checks. Fuel is on and we have fullest tank. Flaps are up, ha ha . . . Altimeter is—damn! Still too high. Get down. What I had not realised is that it takes fewer revs to transport one person at a given

height and speed than it does to transport two people. My normal 2200 revs was too much. By bringing them back the first time and raising the nose I had lost some speed, but I still kept the same height. To heck with it, I just stuck the nose down until she came back to 1000 feet, and decided to worry about avoiding the Cessna in front later. Where was he, anyway? Damn, lost him.

Turning on to base leg I caught sight of him against the ground, well into his final approach. So that was all right. I could forget about him for the present and concentrate on the *grand finale* of the whole performance. Throttle back, hold the nose up to let the speed come back, on with the flap switch, two thirds flap. Little dribble of power back on, and adjust the nose for eighty. Fine. Now where's the runway? A gentle turn on to finals about here should do it. By rights I should now be at around 600 feet. Surprise, I am just that. My tape now records a curiously deep, shuddering sigh, with the words: 'It's all right. We are fine. Just relax . . .'

My memory of the last part is more blurred, probably because I was too busy to notice my feelings and reactions. Down went the last of the flap, and I got her nicely trimmed at 70 knots. I must have been feeling pretty good at this stage, because the 'FOXTROT GOLF, FINALS' sounds eminently languid. A touch of power as we came in over the valley, because she tended to sink like a brick just there. Then, unexpectedly quickly, we had arrived. Nose up a touch to find 65 knots. Cut the power. Bring the stick back. Hold her. Bit more. Hold her. Then, that happy sound of the stall warning buzzer as she quietly decides to stop flying. My tape even recorded the gentle 'phut' of tyre against the runway concrete.

After you have done your solo is the time you really start to learn, I was told when I got in. Maybe. But I have the feeling I learnt a bit just in the five minutes of doing it.

Chapter 18:
Steep turns

The first lesson after going solo was the Steep Turn, another manoeuvre which I found difficult at first. It was explained to me that anything over the 30 degrees of bank used for a medium turn is classed as steep. For this exercise we were going to use 45 degrees of bank.

All the factors which we examined when doing medium turns come into play again. But this time instead of sacrificing speed in the turn we are going to make it good by adding some extra power. The Artificial Horizon is once more the key instrument in the manoeuvre.

There is no mark for 45 degrees of bank on the Cheetah's Artificial Horizon. So we simply aim to get the pointer in between the 30 and the 60 marks. Getting into the turn is a matter of steadily rolling the aircraft, keeping her in balance with the rudder. As the needle passes through the 30 degree bank mark we add a nudge of extra throttle (somewhere between cruising power and full power seemed right). Then the control column is brought back to raise the nose and make good the loss of lift which occurs at this angle of bank (see Chapter 10, Medium Turns, for the explanation of the forces involved). Having reached 45 degrees we hold her there and devote all our attention to making sure that the turn is proceeding as planned, and is not either developing into a spiral dive or a struggling climbing turn which could sooner or later develop into a stall. (As the angle of bank is increased the stalling speed is higher than normal. You

can't help noticing a steep turn increases the effective weight, or loading of the aircraft, something that we can discover easily enough for ourselves as we are pressed firmly down into the seat).

The vital thing in the turn is to keep a sharp lookout at what is happening around us, particularly in the direction towards which we are turning, while simultaneously keeping a watch on the instruments to see that nothing is going wrong. The suggested sequence was to check the Artificial Horizon for the right bank angle, look out, come in to see that the Altimeter was showing a level progress, look out, check the balance, look out, look at the airspeed, look out and do the whole routine again. In addition we shall have half an eye continuously on the Direction Indicator, watching the progress of the turn towards the required heading.

Getting out of the turn involved rolling the wings level, letting go of the rudder pressure to balance the aircraft in straight and level flight, lowering the nose to the normal level attitude and bringing back the power to the normal cruise setting. These steep turns need a bit more anticipation than the medium ones, so I found that beginning the roll out about fifteen degrees before the required heading was necessary in order to avoid having to roll back again.

All this may sound straightforward. But I discovered when we came to try them that they are a lot more difficult to get right than they seem.

First of all it is not easy to put on the bank, bring back the nose and put on the extra power in one, smooth co-ordinated movement. My first fault was not to bring the control column back far enough, so that the nose dropped, the speed picked up, and down we spiralled. It was no good trying to correct this, I found, until I had first taken off some of the bank (back to around 30 degrees), then, having raised the nose, rolled back again.

Then I started to overdo it, particularly doing right hand turns, which were for me far harder than left hand ones. My turns to the right invariably ended up as climbs.

This was easier to correct. A simple nudge forward of the control to lower the nose was all that was needed — but not too much!

After trying some complete circles in both directions I began to get the hang of it, but at the end of the lesson I was far from perfect. It wasn't until I went off to practice them by myself that I discovered my key fault, which was that I was forgetting about applying rudder with the roll to keep the aircraft in balance. An unbalanced aeroplane is far harder to keep under proper control than a balanced one. The knack of bringing extra power, bank and elevators in together is also something that needs some getting used to. The great advantage of having achieved solo status is that at least I can now get permission to go off to a quiet bit of sky and work these things out for myself.

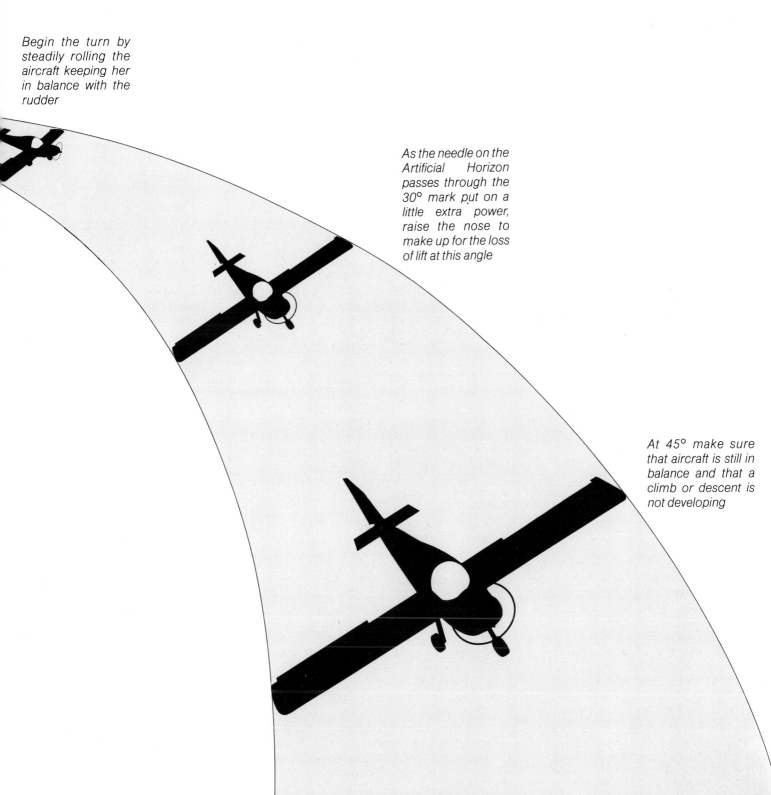

Begin the turn by steadily rolling the aircraft keeping her in balance with the rudder

As the needle on the Artificial Horizon passes through the 30° mark put on a little extra power, raise the nose to make up for the loss of lift at this angle

At 45° make sure that aircraft is still in balance and that a climb or descent is not developing

Chapter 19: Back to the book: ground studies

There is another, earthier, part of the progress towards the PPL that I haven't gone into in any detail yet. It is the set of examinations summed up in the general term 'Ground Studies'. Getting the necessary flying hours and satisfying the examiner in the General Flying Test is only part of the struggle. There are some written tests— three big ones and one small one. If you don't get 70 per cent in one of them you have to sit it again, until you do. But the most important factor about them is that they have all to be taken within six months of sending in your completed licence application. In other words, they should be tackled, ideally, while the flying training is going on.

This is not a text book, so I do not propose to set out all the facts and information needed to pass these exams. There are plenty of publications on the market which do that job much better than I could. (I will give details of the ones I found useful). I will only pass on my own experience when faced with this problem, and would in particular impress one piece of advice: DO NOT TAKE THESE THINGS LIGHTLY. The papers are not difficult, for those who have properly prepared for them. But, as I will to my chagrin relate, it is possible to fail them through lack of preparation and over-confidence. A fairly humiliating procedure then follows. There is a Civil Aviation Authority Form which has to be filled out and signed by the failure, which rests, like some hideous disfigurement, on the unfortunate creature's file, presumably in perpetuity. So before the examination takes place, do revise thoroughly, and approach the exams in the right, serious spirit.

What is involved? In Britain, the papers are these:

1 Air Law. This not only covers the so-called 'Rules of the Air' and the meaning of various signs and signals (roughly analogous to the Highway Code), but also goes into the legal privileges and limitations of the Private Pilot's Licence, the various publications and notices that pilots need to be aware of, numberless technical matters like the various classes of customs facility and when it is obligatory to file a flight plan, as well as procedures for reporting accidents.

2 Navigation and Meteorology. This deals with maps and charts and the art of planning journeys from A to B, taking wind and weather into consideration, with the help of the Navigational Computer. Part of the paper (in my experience the lesser part) deals with the so-called inexact science of weather and what causes it, which demands knowledge about cold and warm fronts, fog and areas of low and high pressure, among other things. When I took it this examination was a one and a half hour paper.

3 Air Tech (i). A wide-ranging paper dealing not only with the principles of flight and the workings of an aeroplane and its engine, but also details of the composition of the element we are most involved with, the air. I also came across questions in this paper dealing with the documentation of aircraft maintenance, which I would normally have expected to find in Air Law. So stand by for surprises and some tricky stinkers.

Air Tech (ii). This is a much simpler and narrower affair, dealing only with the technicalities of the aeroplane in which you are learning and being tested. In my case it required mugging up *The Technical Notes for the AA5A Cheetah* as supplied by the London School of Flying. Things one might be expected to answer are 'How many magnetos does the Cheetah have?' or 'What is the fuel capacity?'

Sets of question papers are issued to official examiners by the CAA which ask a question and in most cases (though not for navigation) supply three alternative answers. On a separate answer sheet the candidate is expected to tick whether the correct solution is 'a', 'b' or 'c'.

What is the best way of overcoming these hurdles? There are several ways.

1 Most of the larger flying schools run a ground studies course for their pupils. I would say this is an excellent method, provided you have the spare time to devote to it. One great advantage will be that you will be getting your wisdom from the people who will be administering your test. I am not suggesting that any preferential treatment or cheating goes on, but it helps to be taught by people who know the kind of tricks that are buried in the examination papers. And I think it is no secret that passing these exams depends a great deal of knowing the kind of thing to expect.

2 You can sit down with the various Civil Aviation Authority pamphlets setting out the required information plus a few text books and try to puzzle the whole thing out for yourself. I don't recommend it. I don't think I am alone in finding that the language of the CAA pamphlets does very little to clarify the situation at all. Early in my studies I was told to acquire from the Stationery Office *Aviation Law for Applicants for the Private Pilot's Licence (CAP 85)*. I did so. Its contents turned my brain to water. Buy it, certainly. But make sure that you have someone at hand to explain what it all means.

3 You can combine working through it on your own with a bit of personal tuition from someone who knows what is involved, preferably your instructor. There will be quite a few days when you turn up for your appointed lesson only to find that the weather has turned nasty. The time can be filled up with some ground study. The advantage here is that you can concentrate on the areas which you personally happen to be weakest at. Another advantage is that you can elect to take your exam at your flying school at just the moment you feel yourself most full of knowledge about that particular subject. You can attack the paper before it all has time to pass into the unconscious, or wherever such things as 'the meaning of a steady red beam aimed at an aircraft in flight near an aerodrome' go about an hour after I think I have learned them. Some instructors also have invaluable lighthearted, short-cut methods of remembering difficult facts which more serious-minded lecturers or publications would feel inhibited to pass on.

4 Or there are courses that can be taken which are quite independent of any airfield or flying club. The advantage here is that they are more convenient for someone who is committed to a full time job in a city. This was my own method. It involved a winter of one evening a week at London's City University, a settled routine which was not too difficult to fit into the timetable of a fairly busy life. The cost when I did it was £50 (though it will certainly have risen by now), and one great advantage was that one could take all the exams on the spot at the end of the course. Other further educational establishments offer similar courses in other cities. There are also some private enterprise efforts, such as the enterprise recently set up in London's Hanover Square called The Fox Aviation School for Technical Studies, run by a lady flying instructor and an ex-Israeli Army nurse called Ronit Fox. Tuition can be had there at various times of the day or evening.

It may possibly be helpful, as a cautionary tale, to relate my own unfortunate experience with these exams. Having spent the winter trooping off one evening a week to the City University I took the papers and passed them all without too much sweat or anxiety. My error was that I did not actually begin the flying part of the business until a bit later. The result was that more than six months had elapsed between taking the papers and passing my General Flying Test., So it was necessary to take them again.

I mugged up my old notes, and with a little personal revision on wet days from Jeanne, I passed first Air Law, then Navigation and Meteorology. My pass marks were not brilliant, but they were adequate. I should have seen the danger signs.

Air Tech (i) had always been my favourite and best subject. Did I not get 98 per cent in the original test? No one could tell me anything about the composition of the atmosphere (Nitrogen 78 per cent, Oxygen 21 per cent, Other gases 1 per cent), the use of an aerodynamic balance on a control surface (to reduce the force needed to move the control by the pilot), or the effect of an exhaust valve sticking open in flight (rough running and a misfiring noise in the exhaust system). So I did about fifteen minutes of revision on my own, and missed out any

session with an instructor altogether. Result? The paper, when it was put before me, prised open large gaps in my knowledge. 'I have bad news for you' said the examiner, as he brought it back. I had managed only sixty-six per cent. And yet I had given the wrong answer to questions which I should, with a bit more thought and attention have got right. I even managed to mess up a question about which way the scoop for supplying fresh air ventilation to the cabin is normally directed. Before me on the wall of the booth in which I was doing the exam was a poster of a Cheetah, with its fresh air scoop pointing plainly forwards into the airstream: And yet I put a tick against 'backwards' into the airstream'. Similarly I have known most of my adult life that in an internal combustion engine a sparking plug sparks shortly before the piston reaches top dead centre (the gases needing a bit of time to ignite before supplying the required explosion). Why then should I put a tick against 'after top dead centre'?

This failure put out, quite unnecessarily, my whole PPL programme. The experience is passed on as a warning that these papers should be prepared for.

Apart from any notes issued by the various ground studies courses at institutions or flying schools I found the following books of value: *Private Pilot Studies* by S. E. T. Taylor and H. A. Parmar, published by T. & A. D. Poyser Limited, Berkhamsted (£4 when I bought it). There is a certain raciness of tone to it, which I found refreshing. It even manages to inject a bit of humour into the subject of aviation law. As an ever-faithful standby I used Volume 4 of Birch and Bramson's *Flight Briefing for Pilots,* already referred to. It includes some photographs of clouds which help to make sense of meteorology and also some useful coloured drawings of the ground signals normally displayed at airfields. It also includes a special way of using the navigational computer to calculate a true heading and ground speed, which involves far less fiddling than the method usually taught. (More about that when we come to cross-country flying).

But I still believe that there is nothing better than someone sitting down to go through the whole thing who is capable of offering

little tit-bits which stick in the mind, That way, the chances of failing the vital examinations are safely minimised.

How do I know, for instance, that a sign like this:

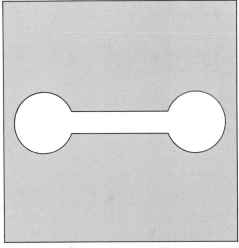

means 'Landing and taking off on runways only. Taxying on grass prohibited', while a sign like this:

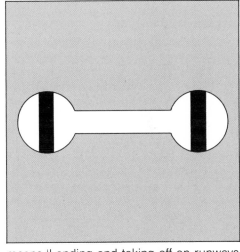

means 'Landing and taking off on runways only, but taxying on grass permitted? Because those two black bars could be marks on the concrete made by tyres picking up dew from wet grass, yes?

And why does a large letter 'C' at an aerodrome signify 'Pilot's Reporting Point'? Not because it stands for 'coffee', but because it means 'Come here'.

That kind of thing will not be found in Civil Aviation Publication No. 85.

Chapter 20: Aerial calamities: the forced landing

I was not allowed to fly solo outside the circuit area until one other lesson had been performed to perfection: the Forced Landing Without Power. The likelihood of finding oneself with a suddenly silent engine while doing some solo cross-country work is small. But it is as well to know what to do if it does happen. Apart from the life-saving aspect the exercise is a useful test of skill and coolness in the air.

We began with our usual ground discussion. Imagine we are flying at 2500 feet across-country when the engine splutters and gives up altogether.

1 The first thing, before any search for a field or looking to see what is wrong, is to get the aeroplane into a steady, trimmed glide at eighty knots. It has got to be in a position to fly by itself from now on. We shall have our hands full doing other things. The last thing we want is to have to wrestle with the aeroplane. So a good, well-trimmed 80 knots is what we are looking for. The natural reaction is to start by picking a field and plunging towards it should be resisted. The less you have to do to keep flying, the more time you will have to find a landing space.

For the purposes of the exercise we shall also be pulling out the carburettor heat to hot and putting on the electrical fuel pump at this stage (though we would get to that a bit later in the real thing).

2 Having got the glide settled the next thing is to look for somewhere to land. There is even a systematic drill for doing this, as shown by the following diagram:

What we are looking for is the biggest field we can see within the gliding distance of the aeroplane, in other words, fairly close. It is better not to waste time and height turning the aeroplane, although this may be unavoidable. More efficient is to study the four

Pick a landing site in this sequence

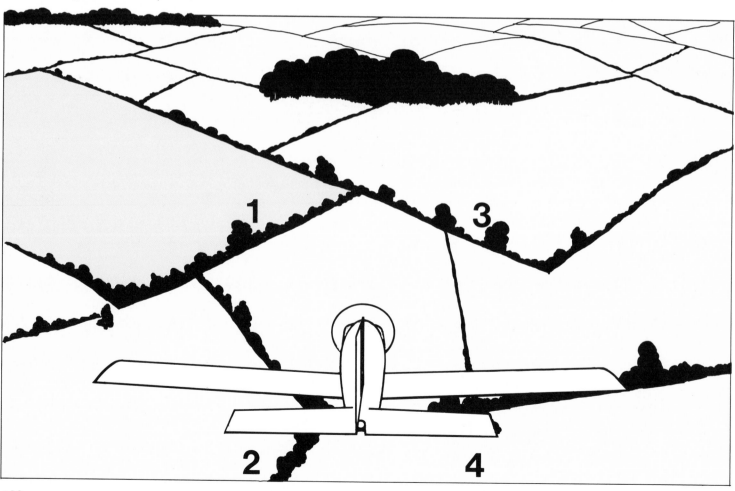

quarters of the ground in the sequence shown by the drawing (assuming we are sitting in the left-hand seat). As a rough guide to distance, we want a field that appears inside the wing tip of the Cheetah (this wouldn't work for a high wing aircraft like the Cessna 150, of course). Outside the wing tip is too far away.

As well as size we are looking for a good surface. Standing crops are not a good choice. Ploughed fields will do in an extremity, if you arrange things so that you come in along the furrows, although they can be too soft for comfort. Early autumn is the best time to have an engine failure, when lots of glorious acres of hard, dry stubble are asking to be used. Normally the choice will have to fall on a piece of promising grassland, preferably without cows on it. Apart from getting in the way they will probably want to come

and take a few inquisitive nibbles from the aeroplane once you have got down. If it slopes uphill, so much the better. Obstructions, like high tension electricity wires, must be avoided. For obvious reasons the field must have a good, clear approach to it.

It is probable that we shall have the wind direction in the back of our mind, but some local smoke should tell us if we don't. The approach should be planned into wind, although fields do not always oblige by having their longest extent laid out along the wind direction. A cross-wind is permissible, but on no account is anything to be attempted with a wind up the tail.

3 Now comes the planning of the approach. Just as in the glide approaches to the airfield we need to select a 'base area', or '1000 feet area' from which we can easily glide into the

chosen field. One vital thing to remember is that the Altimeter will probably be set to the QNH, showing altitude above sea level. So it is necessary to know the height of the ground beneath in order to work out when the aircraft is 1000 feet above its base area. Around the parts of Hertfordshire in which we practised this exercise the ground is about 300—400 feet, so we shall be looking for around 1400 feet on the QNH.

4 Having got everything ready for the worst it is time to see what has gone wrong. We may merely have flicked a switch off with the map, or the passenger could have yanked out the mixture control under the impression it was the cabin heat. In which case, the problem can be cured and the flight continued. For the sake of simplicity I was taught to take things systematically, working from right to left of the cockpit.

Problem check list

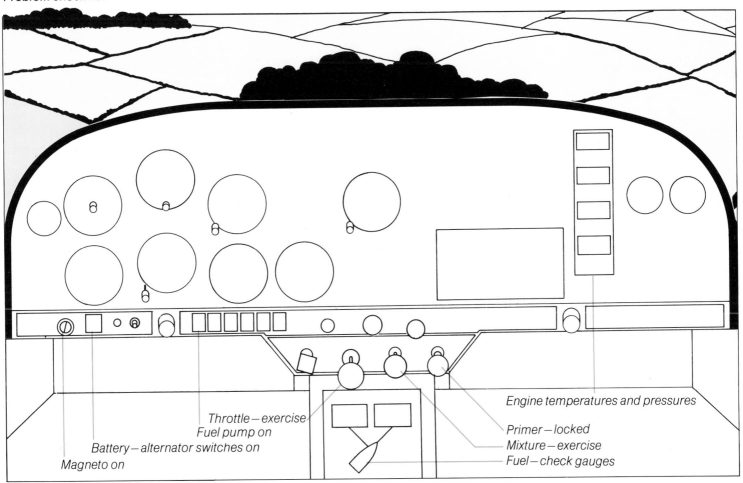

Throttle — exercise
Fuel pump on
Battery — alternator switches on
Magneto on

Engine temperatures and pressures

Primer — locked
Mixture — exercise
Fuel — check gauges

So we start over on the right with the engine temperatures and pressures, which should tell some kind of story. Then back left with the Primer (is it locked?), the Mixture (pull it back and push it in again), the Throttle (same thing) and down to the Fuel Gauges and Fuel Tank Selector. Having had a look at the contents we change tanks and put the electric fuel pump on (the mechanical one could have failed). We would then come fully left to the engine switches, checking that battery and alternator were on and that the magnetos were too. If this rapid tour fails to unearth the problem and get the engine going again, it is time to carry on with the forced landing. (In the exercise these checks are not going to discover any problem, of course, and we are going to carry on with landing preparations anyway).

5 While doing the checks we keep one eye on progress towards the 'Thousand Feet Area'. Having done them it is time to assess the situation. Are we a bit short of height? If so, it might be advisable to cut short the trip to the 'Thousand Feet Area', cut off the corner and head straight for our field. There will probably be a need for constant readjustments, but one thing that we should stick to is our target field. It very rarely pays to make a change of plan about that.

6 Now there should be a breathing space to make the emergency call on the radio to whomever we happen to be tuned into and were last talking to. The call starts with the three magic words which concentrate the mind of the listener and clear everybody else off the air: MAYDAY—MAYDAY—MAYDAY.

Then follows the name of the station we are addressing, our own call sign, what is wrong, what we are doing about it, where we are and how many people on board. So the complete message might go something like this: 'MAYDAY—MAYDAY—MAYDAY, this is Golf Alpha Bravo Victor Charlie, total engine failure, am making forced landing three miles south of Potters Bar, two souls on board'. (The last bit of information, I was told, is so that people don't go plunging into burning wreckage looking for people who aren't there at all).

As soon as we have done that help, plus umpteen fire engines, will be on the way.

7 Time for another check on progress. We should probably be over the 'Thousand Feet Area'. In a practice exercise we give a burst of power at 500 feet intervals to warm the engine. It is helpful to check that the engine is still happy. If left neglected for too long we might discover that it was sulking and refusing to open up when we need to pull away at the end of the exercise. Some crafty students also use this burst of power to give themselves a bit of height and make good any error of judgement they have made in the glide, but most instructors are wise to this one. Ideally we should have plenty of height in hand to land well into the field. If we are sure we are going to make it we can put on some flap, which will steepen the descent. If we have far too much height in hand there are other ways of dissipating it, such as weaving on the approach, or even turning parallel to the field and then back in to it again. We should always make any turns into the field, rather than away from it. At no time should we lose sight of it. Side-slipping is another way of losing height fast, but that is a technique not often taught, now that flaps are fitted to aircraft.

8 The final stage before the landing proper is the moment for the pre-crash checks ('crash' being used fairly loosely, of course). Basically they involve turning everything off, throttle, mixture full out (i.e. to idle cut-off position), fuel off, fuel pump off, mags off, canopy unlocked, harnesses tight. If you have passengers calmly request them to remove their glasses. Lastly, having finished with flaps and radio, it's off with the battery master and alternator switches.

In training (when we should only pretend to turn things off, of course) the instructor will say about now that it is time to pull away. The rule says we mustn't be less than 500 feet above the ground. So it is in with the carb heat and on with full power, getting the flaps up in stages if we have used them and avoiding any houses or sensitive groups of cattle as we roar away.

We began doing some forced landings without power (having found a necessarily deserted part of the countryside), with Jeanne demonstrating the whole procedure and then nominating a field for me to get into. This allowed me to concentrate on

getting the checks and radio call right, without having to worry about choosing a landing spot. After one or two of these the test became harder. I would be flying on a straight and level course not knowing exactly when the throttle would be pulled out. We finally came home and had a pretend engine failure above Elstree, so that I was able to make a complete 'forced landing' on the runway.

These drills continued over several outings, until the process became natural and unhurried. There were times, though, when I found myself concentrating so hard on getting into the field that I would miss out the Mayday call, or forget the pre-crash checks. Such a lapse would be enough to upset an examiner, I was warned.

Pre-crash checks

Battery master and alternator switch ————

Magnetos ————
Fuel pump ————

Throttle ————
Mixture ————

Fuel ————

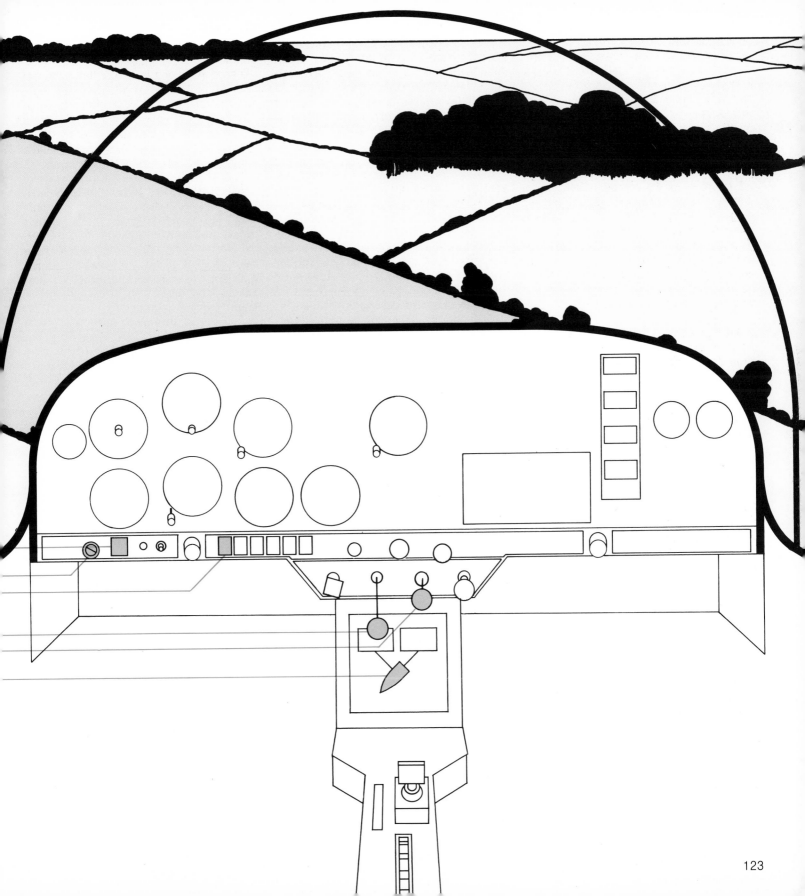

Chapter 21:
Out and about: planning a cross-country flight

Armed with my Airtour Navigational Computer, a ruler scaled in nautical and statute miles, a protractor and an up-to-date 1:500,000 aeronautical chart of Southern England and Wales (known as 'the half million map') I presented myself in the briefing room to prepare a flight plan for my first cross-country run.

Three other pieces of equipment are necessary. A red 'Chinagraph' style of pencil, capable of making a line on the glossy map surface (and also capable of being rubbed off again); an ordinary pencil, for filling in the flight plan and making notes; and a watch which clearly shows the minutes (though it is not necessary at this stage to sport one of those multi-dialled monsters seen upon the hairy wrists of airline pilots and astronauts).

To all this I added a piece of optional equipment of my own, a knee-board with a clamp for fixing papers on it which fastens round the thigh with a 'Velcro' strip and makes it easier to take notes and jot down details while actually flying the aeroplane.

It was then only necessary to collect a London School of Flying VFR (Visual Flight Rules), Flight Plan, borrow the met forecast from the noticeboard for a moment, and start planning my route out and return for my first cross-country flight at the controls.

There is a section of the flying community who will regard what follows now as archaic and faintly ridiculous. When a minimum of radio navigational equipment can free a pilot of all the anxiety of trying to check his position and fly a track by peering at a map why bother with all this line drawing? I haven't been around long enough to join in this argument. It is certainly true that anyone I have flown with around Britain or Europe lately has been tuning into radio beacons rather than sweating over a map, even in the finest weather.

So it could be that we will never bother with any of this again, once the licence is safely secured. But I, personally, found that one of the greatest satisfactions in flying was to draw a line on a map, make some calculations, take to the air, make some more calculations, and discover to my eternal amazement that I arrived at the point I had been aiming for. It is also a fact that 123 pilots got so badly lost in the twelve months of 1981 that they had to make use of the special emergency Distress and Diversion Unit at RAF West Drayton (found by tuning into the emergency 121.5 frequency) asking to be found. So some people are still flying from A to B the hard way. Also, it is worth remembering, radio aids have been known to stop working, and then where are you?

Our first trip was to be on one of the school's well worn triangular courses: Elstree—Clacton-on-Sea—Southend—Elstree. We wouldn't be stopping anywhere. Just getting there and back would be enough for the moment at my stage.

According to the met report the weather was going to be fine, with good visibility and no cloud at our projected altitude of around 2000 feet. The wind at 2000 feet was forecast as 240/15, meaning it should blow from 240 degrees at 15 knots. As a first step we can therefore write 240/15 opposite 2000 in the W/V column, top left corner of the Flight Plan. The forecast also gives the outside air temperature at that height, +7 degrees, so we can write that in as well. We can also put down our I.A.S. (Indicated Airspeed), which is the speed we choose to cruise at: 100 knots. (As we shall see in a minute that is not the true airspeed we shall be flying at, but we are coming to that). So it looks as though we

shall have the wind behind us as we sweep off to Clacton, but that it will be more of a slog on the way home.

Now comes the time to start drawing on the map. Straight lines linking Elstree, Clacton, Southend and back to Elstree will do for a start. The first step is to make a study of the map in order to discover the MSA, or Minimum Safe Altitude. This is defined as being 1000 feet above the highest object within 10 nautical miles of our proposed track. A search of the chart is required, and it helps to draw a couple of lines parallel to the track and 10 miles each side of it, so that we can see what area of the chart we need to be looking at. (The ruler with nautical miles marked to the scale of 1:500,000 helps here). Having found that a 'lighted obstruction' 925 feet high appears to be the highest thing on the Elstree Clacton stretch we can write in 1925 for that section, and the appropriate other heights for the other stretches. It is then advisable to rub these '10 mile' lines out, as they can cause confusion.

Next comes 'Altitude', which we choose to be 2400 feet for all three legs.

Tr(T) stands for True Track. We can measure it on the map between Elstree and Clacton with the protractor (a square, navigational one is best) in the approved way as being 082°. (The theory of all this is explained in Ground Studies courses and text books. I am assuming a bit of knowledge here).

TAS is the 'true airspeed', which because of the effect of pressure and temperature will not be quite the same as the speed shown on the Airspeed Indicator. But by setting the air temperature (+7°) and the height (2400 feet) on the Navigation Computer we can discover that the True Air Speed will in fact be 102 knots, which doesn't make all that much difference to the calculations, but is worth taking account of just the same. (At greater heights the difference between IAS and TAS can be much more significant). So, we put down TAS: 102.

Hdg(T) is the True Heading we need to steer in order to proceed along the track of 082°, bearing in mind that the wind at 240° will be blowing slightly over our right shoulder.

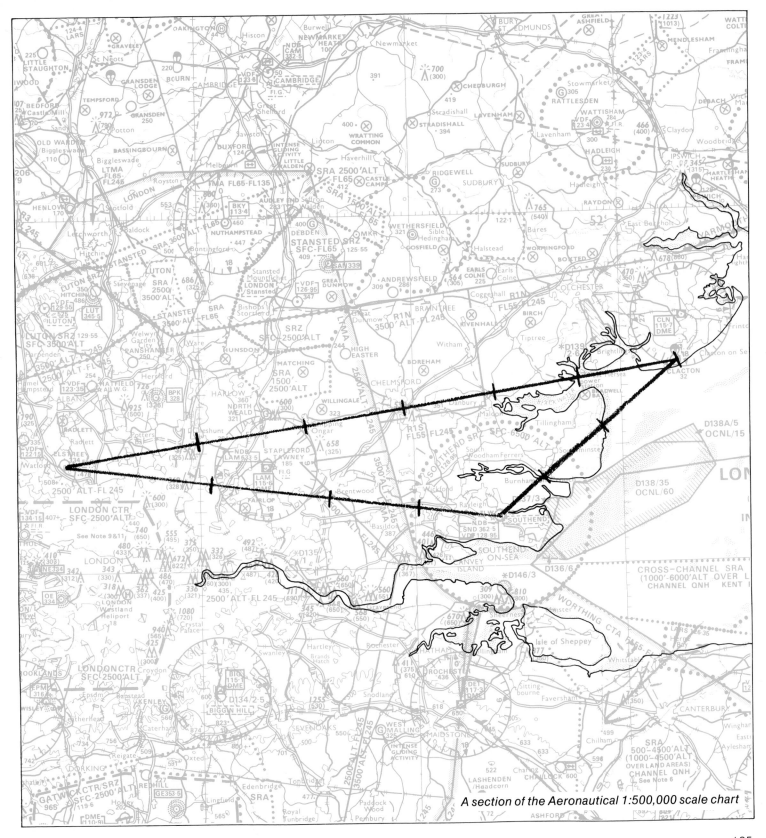

A section of the Aeronautical 1:500,000 scale chart

Having been given the wind speed/direction and the required track our computer will give us the answer, whether we are using the old circular sliderule/fan lines and pencil mark type or a push-button electronic navigation calculator. (Or, for those who want to be really basic, there is the option of getting a bit of scaled graph paper and drawing out a so-called 'Triangle of Velocities', an exercise I can dimly remember from my schoolboy Air Training Corps days). My answer came out at 085° for the first leg, which involves only a very slight aim off for a wind coming almost up our tail. But that is a True Heading. We shall be steering it with the assistance of the compass, so we need to know the magnetic variation in order to convert it into a magnetic heading – Hdg(M). The Magnetic Variation is marked for various areas on the chart by straight lines of purple dashes. We need to pick one of these lines (which as alert

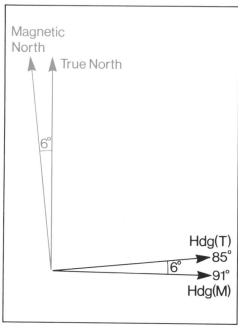

Magnetic variation

Ground Students will know are called 'Isogonals') which cuts through the area of our flight and read off the magnetic variation which it represents (a figure found at the end of the line in the chart's margin). In this case the variation was 6°W, which needs to be added on to the True Heading to give a Hdg(M) 091 degrees.

The computer will also have given us the actual speed over the ground, so that can be entered in at G/S (ground speed). That little bit of wind behind us pushes our speed up to 114 knots. Having measured the distance as 55 nautical miles, it is an elementary matter to discover with a bit of wheel turning on the computer that this will take 29 minutes.

The same details and calculations can now be entered for the other two legs, Clacton – Southend and Southend – Clacton. When all three Magnetic Headings have been marked down it is a useful trick to highlight them with a box drawn in red chalk, because these are the figures we are going to steer by. In the heat of the moment it is all too easy to pick the wrong column and start steering by the Groundspeed.

We now know how much flying time the whole journey will involve. Adding the legs together and allowing an extra 45 minutes reserve for getting lost or being forced to divert brings it up to 116 minutes. At the Cheetah's cruise consumption of 7½ gallons an hour (although she can in fact be made to do better than that) the fuel required works out at a minimum of 14.5 gallons. So that goes into the 'Fuel' column.

So much for the figure theory. The next stage involves some close study of the track on the map. We need some notable landmarks *en route* which can be easily identified and thus confirm whether we are steering the right heading, or not. We can then mark these off, measure the distance between them, and calculate the time it will take to progress from one to the other. In this way we can work out an accurate plot, with estimated times of arrival for each stage of the journey. The first prominent landmark turned out to be my old friends the Lee Valley reservoirs. So down they went in the 'Position' and 'Observation' columns, a distance of 12 miles which should be reached in six minutes.

This first check mark is important. If we can start off going in more or less the right direction the chances are that we shall continue to do so (though winds can suddenly change, of course). What happens if we find we aren't going in the right direction? We'll come to that.

Having marked in check marks for all three legs, with the appropriate distances and times marked in (not forgetting that the ground speed is likely to be different for each leg), it remained to have another look at the chart and mark in the radio frequencies of the various air traffic control facilities which we might encounter *en route*. The only zone we were due to enter was the Southend Airport controller's patch. He could be

VFR FLIGHT PLA

Altitude	W/V	
00´		
2000´	240/15	
5000´		

From	To	
ELSTREE	CLACTON	
CLACTON	SOUTHEND	
SOUTHEND-O·S	ELSTREE	

Position	Obse...	
LEE VALLEY	L. RESERVOIRS	
CHIPPING ONGAR	O/HD. SMALL	
CHELMSFORD	LARGE TOWN	
MALDON	TOWN BY E...	
WEST MERSEA	COASTAL TO...	
CLACTON	A/FIELD BY L...	
COAST LINE	C/ LINE	
BURNHAM	SMALL TOWN	
SOUTHEND	LARGE TOWN ON...	
BASILDON	LARGE TOWN...	
BRENTWOOD	LARGE TOWN...	
S. EPPING FOREST	FOREST TO...	
ELSTREE	RES. S. OF A...	

contacted on 128.95 (the frequency is found on the map). But as we were skirting both the Luton and Stansted Zones we put them in as well for reference. We were also passing close overhead the small airfield of Stapleford Tawney, so that was added. We also noted 'London Director 119.9', a helpful gentleman (also known as 'Heathrow Director') keen to offer guidance to anyone experiencing navigational problems in the vicinity of the London Control Zone. He would prefer to spend a few moments locating us on his Radar screens and pointing us in the right direction rather than have a stray Cheetah bumbling into the path of his Jumbo jets. We also put down the Emergency frequency, 121.5, as a memory jogger in case of the need for a Mayday call.

Having checked the notice board to see if anything special was happening on our route, or if there was a Royal Flight scheduled to cross our path (they merit a special 'Purple Airway', which has to be avoided), we were ready to take an aircraft and start the usual painstaking business of setting off. But this time, with the added anticipation of going somewhere.

Airfield	ELSTREE		
R/W	27R		
QFE	1006		
QNH	1017		
App	1224		
Twr			

JA.S.Kts.
100 Kts

Regional QNH	

SA	Alt.	Tr°T	TAS	Hg°T	Var.	Hg°M	G/S	Dist.	Time	Fuel
25	2400	082	102	085	6°W	091	114	55 mm	29	
6	2400	232	102	233	6°W	239	86	21	15	
25	2400	278	102	272	6°W	278	88	39	27	
								RESERVE	45	
									116 mins	14·5 GALLS

	Dist.	Time	ETA	ATA
T	12	6 mins	32	33
+RIVER	10	5	38	38
ON RT.	8	4	42	42
Y	8½	4½	46½	46½
	8½	4½	51	51
ON COAST	9	5	56	58
	9	6	04	04
OF ESTUARY	6½	4½	08½	08½
(WITH PIER)	5	3½	12	12
HALL ON.RT.	7½	5	17	17
STH (RAIL)	7½	5	22	22
H	10½	7	29	28
D	13	9	37	

Notes

GBG5K IS AN AA5A NAVIGATION EXERCISE FROM ELSTREE TO CLACTON & SOUTHEND & RETURN. PRESENTLY 4 NMILS S.W OF CLACTON AT 2400° ON QNH 1017. HEADING 240 ESTIMATE PASSING OVERHEAD SOUTHEND AT 13 . REQUEST TRANSIT CLEARANCE THROUGH THE ZONE.

200FT QNH 1017

Facility	Freq.
ELSTREE	122·4
STAPLEFORD	122·8
STANSTED ZONE	125·55
SOUTHEND APP	128·95
LONDON DIV	119·9
LUTON	129·55
EMERGENCY	121·5

Having taken off, the first thing to do was to climb up to the alititude chosen for the flight and pass over the middle of the airfield at that height. We could then take up the first heading and check the time of departure. This involved a long gentle climbing turn to the right, cunningly judged so that I arrived at 2400 feet just in time to turn on to 091° on the Direction Indicator, a feat which was asking too much of me, I fear. Having missed the airfield first time I went round again and set off, with the needle of the DI swaying round about the 090 mark (no-one is expected to steer to within one degree, anyway). Just in the nick of time I remembered to look at my watch, and saw it was 11.26. That meant I should be over the Lee Valley in

between the chain of reservoirs at '32', by my mental arithmetic. I noted it down in the ETA column of the Flight Plan.

It was now time to do some FREDA checks, the general set of checks used to ensure that things are as they should be while en route to our destination.

F for Fuel. We had plenty, were on the right fullest tank, and as we were facing a lengthy spell of cruising at altitude there was the opportunity to do some 'leaning off' of the mixture to save fuel. Oh, and we could turn the auxiliary electric fuel pump switch off for the moment, and rely on the suction fuel supply.

R for Radio. It was time to say goodbye to Elstree and announce that we would 'call again on re-join'.

E for Engine. Temperatures and pressures OK? Revs correct? Everything seemed to be humming sweetly.

D for Direction Indicator. Check that it is synchronised with the magnetic compass. We had wandered away from 090 during the past activities. I lurched her back again.

A for Altimeter. It is set to the QNH? Yes. We seemed to have gained a hundred feet, so I settled her back down to our cruising altitude of 2400 feet again.

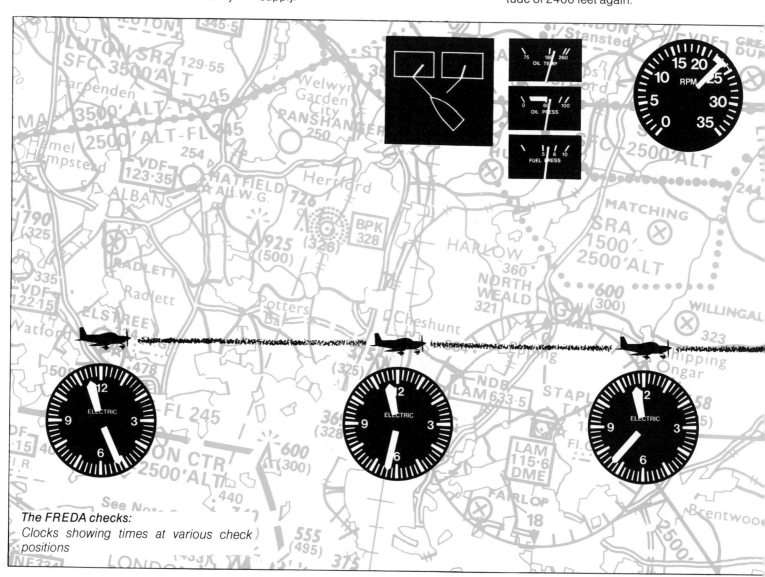

The FREDA checks:
Clocks showing times at various check positions

With all these vagaries and inaccuracies it was a surprise to see the correct spot between the reservoirs coming up straight ahead. We arrived only one minute later than expected, at '33'. I wrote that down in the ATA (actual time of arrival) column, then went down to the next line and wrote 38 for ETA at Chipping Ongar.

All this may sound a fairly cool procedure. In my case it was accompanied by such things as dropping pencils beneath the seat, and scrabbling around to find them while trying to keep the aeroplane on course and at the right height. I learnt that a good firm attachment for a pencil stuck to the side of the cockpit or on the knee-board is a vital aid to navigation. Other mundane matters intruded. What should I do with the map when I needed all my knee space to consult and notate the flight plan log? I found it advisable to fold it into a small, compact shape so that only the area of the journey showed, fastened with an elastic band. It saved having volumes of map festooning the cockpit. It could then be lodged on top of the fascia panel when not needed, easily reached for when a reassuring glance was required.

As can be seen from the plan, everything happened more or less as and when expected. This was an ideal way of being introduced to cross-country flying. There were plenty of clearly recognisable features on the route, so that there were never any moments of anxiety about where we actually were. Every town has its 'signature', a special feature easily visible from the air, which identifies it to the pilot for all time. I shall now always think of Chelmsford, for instance, as a 'large town with reservoir due south'. Sheets of water appeared as the most easily identifiable landmarks. Our whole journey was framed by the Thames Estuary over to the south, emerging from the tower blocks of the City. The shape of islands in the Blackwater Estuary and the way Burnham sits on the Crouch all did their bit to confirm the route. Thus, my first cross-country flight was visually reassuring, if nothing else.

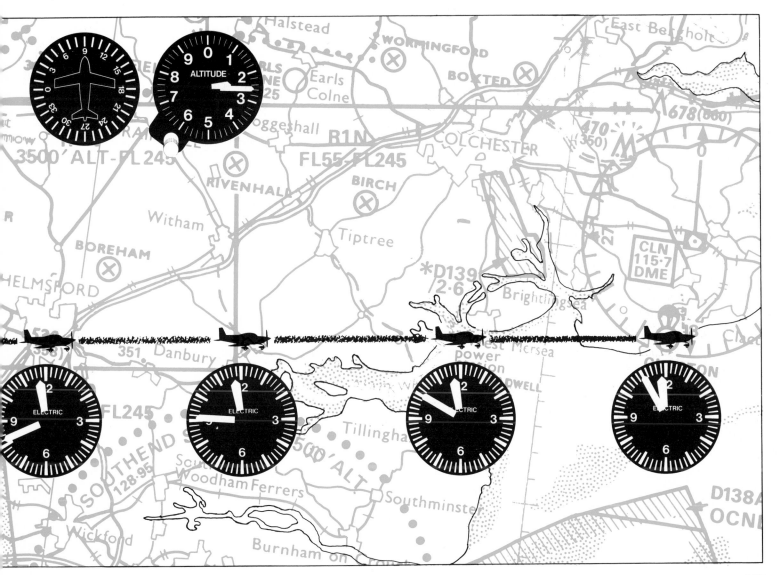

Heading out to sea from Clacton towards Southend was the moment to prepare the radio message announcing our arrival at the Zone boundary (which should be delivered at least ten minutes before the Zone boundary is reached). Jeanne helpfully wrote the standard message out for me in the notes section of the Flight Plan. This did not prevent me from committing the howler of calling them up with the greeting: 'Stansted, this is Golf Bravo Golf Sierra Kilo'. The slightly hurt response came 'Golf Sierra Kilo, if you want Stansted it's on one two fife decimal fife fife'. 'Correction, Southend this is Golf Bravo Golf Sierra Kilo . . .'.

Having got that sorted out I launched forth with the slightly halting information that 'Golf Sierra Kilo is an AA5A on navigation exercise from Elstree to Clacton and Southend and return. Presently 4 nautical miles south-west of Clacton at 2400 feet on QNH 1017, heading 240, estimate passing overhead Southend at one three and request transit clearance through the Zone'. Would I be routing direct to Elstree from Southend, I was asked? 'Affirmative'. 'Report 2000 feet above the field on QNH 1018'. 'Roger, Sierra Kilo'. This involved a change of one millibar

on the Altimeter setting, and a gentle loss of height as we approached the large runway clearly visible in front of the conglomeration of Southend.

The last leg was the hardest from the map-reading point of view. One bit of North-East London surburban sprawl looks very much like another. But the airfield of Stapleford Tawney came up in more or less the correct position over to the right, while over the nose glittered the friendly reservoirs. The final stage was to do the pre-landing checks and call up Elstree in order to announce our return requesting the current circuit information. It was still runway 27, with Right-Hand Circuit. So I went through the standard rejoin procedure of letting down to circuit height (on the aerodrome QFE) on the left-hand, or 'dead' side, crossing the upwind threshold of the runway at exactly 1000 feet, and joining the circuit downwind, making sure to keep a good lookout for other aircraft all the time. This is not the time to relax altogether.

Four or five other cross-country trips, dual and solo, followed, culminating in the so-called 'Cross-Country Qualifying Test', which

involves a triangular course with two intermediate stops, one of them being at least 50 nautical miles from the home airport.

In the process of doing these I experienced a few moments of tension, when expected landmarks failed to materialise, though I was usually saved by the appearance of something recognisable before long. As confidence grew I was able to cope with the unexpected, such as arriving at Cambridge and being told to 'use the grass as the runway is temporararily blocked'. The grass? Which bit of grass? 'Cambridge, could you confirm position of your grass runway, please. Sierra Kilo'. 'Sierra Kilo, the grass runway runs alongside the main runway to the left, repeat left'. 'Roger, Sierra Kilo'. I had luckily been given some grass landings and take-offs shortly before to prepare for such an eventuality. The temptation with grass is to hold off too high, because the textured surface of the ground makes it seem closer than it really is.

Things I tended to forget were the lining up of the Direction Indicator and Compass every fifteen minutes. Failure to do this on one occasion made me nearly miss Cambridge. I

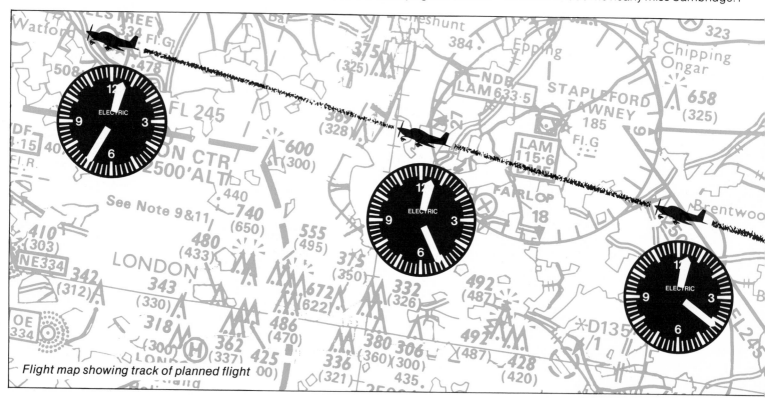

Flight map showing track of planned flight

was heading into the flat wastelands of Huntingdonshire— a hard place to find any landmarks—until I caught sight of King's College Chapel sticking out of some grey murk some way to my right.

There is a set drill to go through if and when I did go astray, the so-called 'Lost Procedure'. Keeping one's head is the main pre-requisite. The first step is to make a note of the time the Procedure begins, then make sure that you are above the minimum safety altitude and that the Altimeter is not telling lies by being on the wrong setting. Then the fuel state is checked, and having made sure that there is no immediate danger of the flight coming to a nasty end one way or another we can begin coolly solving the problem.

There could be what is called a 'gross error', or major blunder; possibly because the Direction Indicator isn't adjusted or because we have picked the wrong figure as our heading from the flight plan. Having checked for this kind of mistake (holding our original heading all the time we are doing the investigating) we can try the so-called 'Circle of Uncertainty' technique. This involves picking a point on the map at which we believe we

ought to be, taking into consideration the last firm fix we entered into the log and the time and direction flown since then. We then draw a ten-mile radius circle round this point. The supreme likelihood is that we shall be within or close to that circle. How do we find out? The best way is to study the ground for prominent recognisable features, and then to look for them on the map. It is fruitful to work from the ground to the map, rather than the other way round. Every time we pick a feature we should make a note of it in the log so that we build up a picture which should help confirm our position when we do find a feature which seems to tally with something on the map. (Intersections of roads and rivers, railways and roads, or all three together, are ideal. But you can't beat a stretch of water). Another method is to search the map nearby for what is called 'a line feature', which is an easily recognisable object stretching for some distance—like a coastline or big wide river, or even a motorway if we can be sure of identifying one. It is then only necessary to fly along this feature until we pinpoint enough landmarks along it to be certain of our position. As a last resort there was always, of course, the radio, to request a position.

On one occasion, I was also given a fresh destination in the middle of a cross country, which involved drawing a new line on the map from my track to the new target, working out the new heading and flying it. There is always the possibility that the target airfield becomes unusable, due to weather or other reasons. It is vital to know how to divert successfully to another one.

Gradually I became aware that there are in fact two kinds of 'Pilot Navigation'. There is the rough and ready kind which more or less gets you there, with a bit of luck and some scrambling through sticky patches. And there is the other kind, which involves keeping a constant check on position and making heading corrections as soon as an error is discovered. The second kind, which usually requires some mental arithmetic *en route* and occasional swivelling of the computer wheel, is by far the most satisfying. (Those wishing to enjoy it must be familiar with a simple piece of mathematics called 'The One In Sixty Rule', a mystery which all ground text books explain).

'But above all, remember this', I was told. 'Being lost is largely a state of mind'.

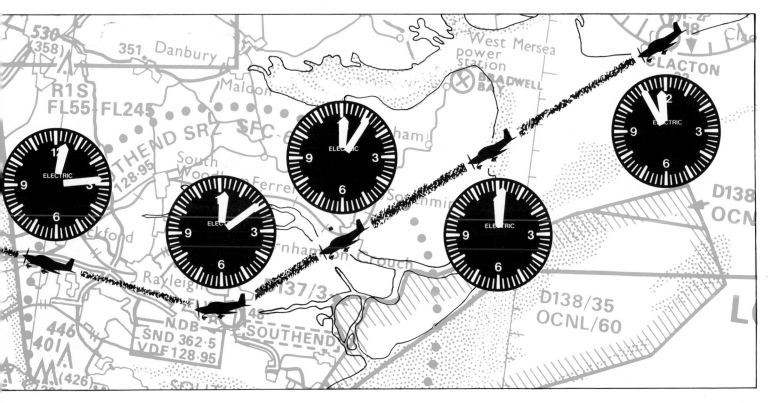

Chapter 22: Flying in poor visibility

Strictly speaking no mere PPL holder should ever get into a position where he, or she, is forced to fly by instruments. Cloud or fog must be avoided by all but those with the training and legally current Instrument Ratings. But sudden deteriorations of the weather do occur. The accident statistics tell a melancholy story of what happens to people who are caught in poor visibility without the experience to handle it. So there has recently been a slight increase in the amount of instrument flying given to PPL students, in order that novice pilots may have some idea of what to do.

In my own case I discovered, unexpectedly, that the process of flying solely by registering the messages being relayed by a set of dials (while totally rejecting the false messages of the senses) has a certain charm. I finally completed quite a number of instrument flying sessions, including an absorbing hour pottering round the mighty Stansted Airport, being talked down by their controller for so-called Radar Surveillance Approaches. (These are not normally in the PPL syllabus, but I suspect the aim was to give me the taste in order that I would be encouraged to go on to further stages of flying training).

The first essential, I was told, is to realise that the human senses are not to be trusted when flying blind. The balance mechanism of the inner ear is capable of telling us things which are simply not true. Without the use of the eyes as a check we are all too ready to be taken in. After a sharp right turn we can imagine we are turning left, for example, when we are flying straight ahead. 'Put your trust in the instruments' is the rule. Do not try to fly by the seat of your pants, but check what the instruments are telling you.

The key to the whole business is the Artificial Horizon.

The symbol across the centre represents the aeroplane. The line across the middle of the dial represents the horizon. So the aircraft symbol lifting above the horizon shows a pitch up of the nose and sinking below it shows a pitch down. A tilt left or right shows left or right bank. The fan lines in the bottom half of the dial help with turning. We merely have to line the bar up with the top sloping line on the left or right side to achieve a modest left or right turn. Parallel with the fan line, but above it, would show a climbing turn, below it a descending turn. Thus, we have a picture of the aircraft's attitude.

In instrument flying I was taught to use much slighter and more restrained control movements than in normal visual flight. For a climb pitching the nose a mere one thickness of the bar above the horizon line is used. At full power that gives a climbing speed of around 100 knots and a rate of climb of only about 400 feet per minute. Equally, a pitch of one bar thickness below

Using the Artificial Horizon when flying by instruments

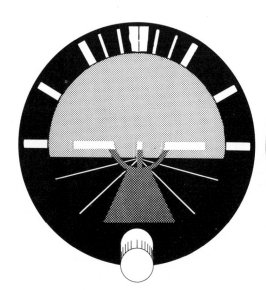

A climb pitch of one thickness of the bar above the horizon. At full power and 100kts indicates a rate of climb of 400ft per min.

A level turn using the top fan line to judge the angle of bank

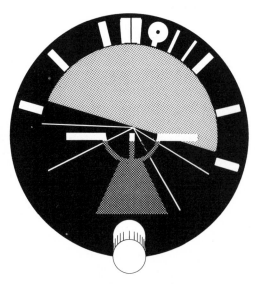

The aircraft symbol tilting below the horizon indicates a descending turn

the horizon is used with around 1900 revs to descend. That takes us down at 100 knots at around 500 feet per minute. So it is all a much gentler business than visual flight.

After the A/H, and working in harness with it, comes the RPM gauge. These two are themselves enough to tell us what is going on, because we remember 'Attitude plus power equals performance'.

If we are flying with a level nose attitude according to the Artificial Horizon and have cruise power of around 2200 revs, then it must follow that we should be maintaining a level flight at around our cruising speed of 100 knots. Cross reference to the Altimeter, the Airspeed Indicator and the Vertical Speed Indicator will confirm it.

Of course, they may not confirm it. Both the Altimeter and Vertical Speed Indicator may be showing a slight sink, in which case we check back again to find out what is happening. An airspeed of more than 100 knots would indicate that we haven't quite got the pitch right and are in a shallow dive.

But if the speed and the pitch seem right, it could mean that we are a bit low on power and should try another 500 revs.

Wearing a hood shaped like an oversize crash helmet with an opaque visor which cut off my sight of everything except the instruments in front of my eyes, we set off to try this out in practice. Jeanne put the aircraft in a level cruise for me, and then I took over to try and hold it there using instruments only. The first thing to learn was to react correctly to what the Artifical Horizon was telling me. This might sound obvious, but it turned out not to be as easy as it seemed. When the symbol showed a tilt to the left of the central horizon line I had an irrational urge to correct it by moving the control column over to the left, which only aggravated the situation. It took time before I made the right correction without having to think about it.

We then tried some climbs and descents, which introduced the concept of the Scan. This is a method of keeping more than one instrument under observation at the same time and ensuring that the total sum of what

they are telling us adds up to the manoeuvre we want. For the climb from straight and level flight we first put on full power (stopping any yaw and keeping the wings level) while letting the aircraft settle into its correct attitude one thickness above the horizon line on the Artificial Horizon. I found there was no need to trim it or apply any real backward pressure on the control column. The extra power took the nose automatically into more or less the right place.

We then proceeded gently upwards while I monitored our progress by means of the Scan. Everyone probably develops their own personal technique for doing it. The idea is to have one group of instruments (four or, at the most, five) under constant surveillance (called the Major Scan), while taking regular looks at one other instrument (called the Minor Scan). The instruments chosen for these Major and Minor Scans depend, of course, on the manoeuvre.

I found it possible to let my eye swivel round the Major Scan, taking the lot in more or less simultaneously (although I was, in fact,

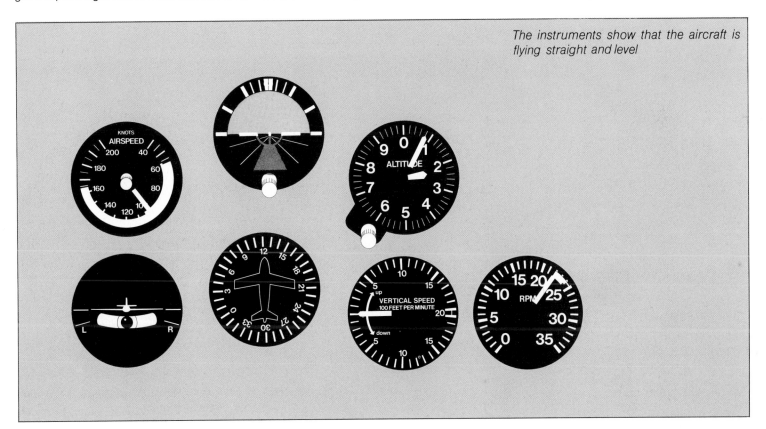

The instruments show that the aircraft is flying straight and level

presented with a suggested route backwards and forwards which the eye should ideally take), while moving over at regular intervals to take a glance at the Minor Scan.

For climbing, the Major Scan involved watching the Artificial Horizon to see that the attitude was right while more or less simultaneously watching the Direction Indicator to see that the aircraft wasn't turning off course, the Airspeed Indicator to see that we were keeping our 100 knots, and the Ball of the Turn and Slip Indicator to make sure she was properly balanced. From time to time I would glance alongside to the Altimeter (Minor Scan), to see how the climb was progressing getting ready to level out just before reaching the required height. This time there was no waiting for the speed to build up in level flight, because we were already doing 100 knots. So I merely had to settle the aircraft symbol back on the horizon line and bring the power back to the cruising revs simultaneously. Then I started another set of Major and Minor scanning for straight and level flight, grouping the Artificial Horizon, the Direction Indicator, the Altimeter and the Slip Indicator in one scan, while taking occasional glances at the Airspeed Indicator to see that we were keeping to 100 knots.

I was warned not to jump to any conclusions and react immediately if one of the instruments seemed to be telling the wrong story. First, the various instruments need to be cross-checked against each other to find out what is wrong. If, for instance, the Artificial Horizon shows the nose is pitched up the correct amount above the horizon line for a climb, but the Altimeter is not showing any gain in height, it would be foolhardy to react by pulling the nose up a bit more and hoping for the best. If the nose is up and we are not climbing that fact must have an effect on at least one of the other instruments, namely the Airspeed Indicator, which ought to show that the speed has decreased, the necessary result of a nose up attitude in level flight. If the speed has dropped off then it is time to look for the cause of the problem elsewhere, namely in the power. Have we got the right revs? Has the throttle vibrated its way back to less than full power? Are the temperatures and pressure telling us any alarming news? A moment's thought will show that pulling the nose up in such circumstances would have been the first foolhardy step on the road to a further loss of speed and possible stall. Maybe even a spin. Getting out of a spin using instruments alone can be done, but is not for beginners.

On another session we did level turns, for which the aircraft symbol is lined up on the top 'fan line', a mere 17° of Bank. This is the equivalent of what is called a 'Rate One Turn' for a speed of 100 knots. A Rate One turn is a manoeuvre which will put the aircraft through 180 degrees in one minute, which is one degree every three seconds. (There is a formula for working out the angle of bank involved in a Rate One turn, it being one tenth of the speed plus seven. Therefore at 100 knots a Rate One will be $10+7=17$ degrees angle of bank). If we didn't have the fan line to help we should have to guess the bank angle by sticking the pointer at the top of the Artificial Horizon just over half-way between the lightly painted ten and twenty degree marks on the dial.

Using a Major Scan for climbing involves simultaneously watching the Artificial Horizon, Direction Indicator, Airspeed Indicator, the ball of the Turn and Slip Indicator, and from time to time, the Altimeter (Minor Scan)

Knowing that three degrees change of heading take one second in a Rate One turn can come in useful in one of the complications of instrument flying, an instrument failure. I was made to fly with a piece of cardboard stuck over the Direction Indicator and the Turn and Slip Indicator, which represented the predicament I would have been in if the gyro suction pump had gone wrong. How would it be possible to judge a turn onto a fresh heading, when the Compass, as we know, goes haywire during an actual turn making it difficult to tell when the new heading has been arrived at? We simply count the number of degrees involved in taking up the new heading, divide by three, put her in a Rate One turn and hold it for that number of seconds. When the Compass has settled down on the new heading we can check whether we got it right and make any adjustments necessary. This seemingly rule-of-thumb method is most helpful and surprisingly accurate.

On the third instrument session we did climbing turns and descending turns, which are quite a lot of things going on at once, particularly when Jeanne devilishly calculated it so that I arrived at the new heading and the new height at the same time, and so had to level out from the turn and level off from the climb simultaneously.

This was all preparation for the big day when we fitted special screens round the inside of the Cheetah's cockpit (which were designed so that an instructor can see out but the student can't) and hopped over to Stansted for some Surveillance Radar Approaches. They do not aim to bring people right down to the runway, but only to a minimum height from which the runway ought to be in view. If it isn't in view then the rule is never to carry on bumbling down into the murk below our declared minimum height, but to overshoot and try again, or even go somewhere else.

The blips on the controller's Radar screen only show distance from the field and direction of travel. They do not show height. So all that can happen is that we are told on the final approach when to begin going down at the correct three degree descent rate (which is what our normal instrument descent should be). As the approach continued he would call out how far still to go, any direction corrections which were needed and what height I ought to be passing through at that point. It was then up to me to check on the Altimeter whether I was going down too fast or too slowly, and make any necessary alterations. As a rough help I had the Vertical Speed Indicator, which at our speed needed to show an average descent of about 500 feet per minute.

Thanks to the patience of the Stansted controller (who was kind enough to say that it was good practice for him, too) I did three of these. It was very reassuring to open up the screens as the minimum height was reached and find the huge Stansted runway stretching out directly in front of the nose.

All this had little to do with the PPL syllabus. But if through my own stupidity, or some unlikely nation-wide flash fog, I get caught in the murk at least I can now head for Stansted (or anywhere else with a Radar talk-down facility) with some hope of saving my neck.

The instruments indicating a level turn, using the top fan line for 17° of bank or a 'Rate One Turn' at 100kts

Chapter 23: Revision time

The two final sessions with Jeanne were devoted to revising. We went through everything we had done, from the early days of holding the aircraft level at different speeds to my more recent struggles with steep turns and banks.

I had arranged to do the flying test with the Elstree Chief Instructor, Captain Mike McDonnell. I was warned that there were one or two things he was particular about. Keeping a conscientious look out at all times was one of them. But another thing which I was informed makes him particularly unhappy involves the touch-and-go landing technique (when a landing is followed by an immediate opening of the throttle and a take-off). On no account forget to put the flaps up before opening the throttle to take off again, I was told. So I practised sweeping my hand over the flap switch on my way to the throttle in order not to be caught out with that one.

My midday date arrived. After a coffee and a bit of quiet contemplation of all that I had to get right I presented myself to the CFI's room. He motioned me to sit down and began to tell me what was in store.

As a start he explained what might be thought the slightly peculiar arranagement, whereby the chief of a flying school is actually responsible for testing the competence of one of the school's pupils. Couldn't there be a clash of loyalties, or a bit of favouritism? The CAA, he said, cannot manage to do all the testing, and so the responsibility is delegated to approved examiners. He likes testing because it is his quality control procedure. He is able to judge in what state the products are being turned out by the individual instructors, and can tighten up any loose instructional points.

His emphasis, he said, would be on safety. Having got a licence I could buy an aircraft and never see an instructor again. He has got to be certain that I am capable of looking after myself in the air without any more briefings or supervision. What he would be looking for would be flying that is 'safe, accurate and comfortable'. It would be a little trip covering general handling plus a little bit of instrument flying. He would not be saying anything, so it would be no use giving him an inquiring glance looking for confirmation or reassurance. I would be on my own. If he reacted at all it would mean that he was frightened by what I was doing.

I would do the document checking and pre-flight checks, then we would take off, fly towards the east and settle down at 2000 feet. Once I had got the aircraft settled and trimmed we would start with some medium turns, followed by some steep turns, some climbing and descending, then up to 2400 feet for some stalling during which he would be looking for recovery with minimum loss of height. Then we should have an emergency engine failure, requiring me to take the appropriate action to save my life and my passengers' lives. Then I would don the hood and do some instrument flying, just climbs, descents and a few turns on to headings. Then back to the airfield, doing the correct

airfield approach procedure and joining in the manner appropriate to the circuit. We would do normal, flapless and glide approaches, with the standard radio procedure. Then we'll sit down and discuss it. 'Right. Let's go and get an aircraft'.

By this time I was beginning to feel the onset of nervous tension. So much so, that as I sat making the radio call for the pre-flight check and taxi clearance I suddenly found that my mind went blank as I came to the bit which required me to relate the captain of the aircraft's name. The sequence went :Golf Alpha Bravo Victor Whisky, pre-flight check and taxi clearance, to the east, captain's name, er, er . . . McDee'.

The consequent laughter helped mop up some of the tension, although the first medium turn was a little shaky and hesitant. After that, though, things seemed to be going very well. Even the steep turns worked, with no nasty spiral dive. As for the Forced Landing Without Power, a very large and agreeable field cropped up just in the right spot, so we were able to make an immaculate glide approach with all checks and emergency calls completed. The rejoin to

the circuit and the landings worked out without too many problems, and as I saw his gaze directed down between the seats as we prepared to go off for another round I duly remembered to flip the flap switch up before opening the throttle. The flapless approach and landing would scarcely have disturbed the skin from the surface of a rice pudding, helped by the fact that it was a beautifully soft, gentle smooth day. All this time there was a total silence from my companion (except for one expletive when he had to grab the controls during my instrument flying sequence in order to avoid an apparently blind twin-engined machine coming the other way). Only as I was about to touch down from the final manoeuvre, the glide approach, did he open up with a display of human exuberance: 'OK, bung down the last bit of flap, hold her off, hold her . . . fine. Well, that was perfectly satisfactory.' As we coasted up the runway I told myself that this might possibly mean that I had passed.

Back in his office he had some comments, however. My use of rudder in the turns was rough, if not outright non-existent. I needed to perfect the smooth, co-ordinated use of rudder and ailerons. I seemed to think that

taxying meant putting the revs at 1,000 RPM and leaving them there, using the brakes to slow down. That was not the way to do it. For slowing down I should throttle down as well, otherwise there was unnecessary brake wear. Also there was no point in swinging from side to side while taxying to the holding point in order to test the turn instruments. I was forced to make several turns taxying along the apron. I could check them then. There was also no point in lowering the nose to accelerate after take off before the climb. Let her climb straight away. Also, I didn't lean off the fuel when settling her down at 2000 feet, although that may have been because I knew we were shortly going to do things which required altered power settings. (It wasn't. I forgot. But I let that pass). 'The forced landing, by the way, was probably the best I have seen on any test'.

So there it was. The culmination of just over two months of surprisingly exhausting concentration on my part. Plus boundless patience on the part of my ever-cheerful instructor. But it was, of course, just the beginning.

Chapter 24:
What do I do when I've passed?

What can I do now I've got my PPL Licence?

Naturally, I had picked up quite a lot of information on what happens next during my flying lessons, but to make quite sure of all the possibilities open to a PPL holder, I had a chat with Steve Read, the business manager of the London School of Flying.

The first thing I discovered, rather to my surprise, was that until recently quite a large percentage of people who have gained their Private Pilot's Licence have stopped right there, and fly very little. It seemed odd to me, having gone through all the effort necessary to qualify for a licence—never to use it, rather like passing a driving test and sitting in the back seat for the rest of your life! This tendency has changed with the advent of self-fly hire fleets.

But as was constantly made clear to me—and to you, if you have read so far—in flying, you never stop gaining experience. And obtaining your licence is just a step along the way. Now you can go on to improve your flying, and earn other qualifications. One of the best post-PPL courses to take, I was told, is the IMC rating. This is a course that teaches the student basic instrument flying in bad weather (Instrument Meteorological Conditions), and is a very useful adjunct to the basic licence, giving the pilot confidence in handling his aircraft should the weather deteriorate during a flight. How necessary this is is confirmed by the accident statistics—more accidents are caused by pilot inexperience in bad weather conditions than stall/spin related mishaps nowadays.

Apart from necessary previous experience as pilot in command, the course given by the

London School of Flying is a fifteen hour one, giving instruction on instrument work and the use of radio navigation beacons, together with instrument approaches to airfields. The pilot takes an examination at the end of his course, and if he passes, he then has his IMC rating.

So far, the qualification is only recognised in Great Britain, and allows the pilot to fly in nil visibility conditions outside controlled airspace and 1½ miles visibility within it provided certain other criteria are adhered to. It does not, of course, replace the full Instrument Rating, which demands a minimum of 150 hours as pilot in command, an approved ground course and examination, plus a forty-hour flight course leading to a practical examination. Many private pilots never reach this level of skill, but it is an essential part of the commercial pilot's licence. I could see from my own experience that the additional IMC Rating would be a very worth-while addition to my basic licence, giving me confidence in my ability to get out of trouble if I met bad weather while on a cross-country flight. It also makes for extended use of aircraft if we are not grounded by doubtful weather conditions such as haze or cloud.

There are also courses offered to convert to multi-engined or complex aircraft, and this would probably be the next step if you were going to use the aircraft for business, or wanted to go on towards a commercial pilot's licence. But further training apart, what do people do about flying themselves once they have their PPL? Steve Read told me that 25 per cent give up flying, 5 per cent buy aircraft, 10-15 per cent go in for group ownership, and the rest—about 55 per cent—rent aircraft on self-fly hire.

What are the advantages and disadvantages of these methods for getting into the air, The most popular is self-fly hire, I was told. Here all the worry and capital and incidental costs are taken off the pilot's shoulders, and all he does is pay for actual flying time—with a basic minimum number of hours depending on the length of time he wants the aircraft. The pilot knows that he will be flying a properly maintained, well-equipped aircraft, and, if anything should go wrong with it, there will be a substitute 'plane available. Some hire fleets offer a preferential

scheme—by becoming a member, aircraft may be priority booked, and hired 'dry'—that is, fuel put in at the pilot's expense, which can give useful rebates if the fuel is purchased abroad. And, in that case, there are duty-free goods to purchase. If the pilot has not flown with the company before, he is checked out on the type of aircraft before being allowed to fly off with a valuable aeroplane. Self-fly hire makes a lot of sense if you are not flying more than about a hundred hours a year.

The next most popular way of flying yourself is the group scheme, in which a number of individuals join together to purchase and maintain an aircraft. The advantages are that the capital cost is shared, and the bills for maintenance and aerodrome fees for parking and landing are also divided up among the members of the group. Snags may arise when everybody wants to fly at once—after all, for the less-experienced pilot, the days when weather conditions are perfect are not all that many—and the unlucky partner may become discouraged and sell out, which may lead to personality clashes when the original membership is diluted by outsiders. And if four people own an aircraft, and fly about twenty-five hours each, the costs come to about the same per hour as hiring the aircraft, plus all the bother and responsibility of owning the aeroplane. You need to be very sure that you will get on well with your partners, and do enough flying to make group ownership really worthwhile.

Finally, there is the individual owner. According to what I was told, private owners represent a minority in Britain, and most of them use their aircraft for business. It is possible to obtain an aircraft mortage, repayable over five to seven years, and this offers tax attractions to businesses and self-employed people. Most business pilots, I was informed, buy a high-priced single-engined 'plane, but quickly pass on to a twin-engined aircraft if they are doing much long-distance business flying, particularly over water. There is a six-hour conversion course available. It is possible to buy an aircraft and enter into a rent-back arrangement with a flying school or hire fleet operator, which will maintain the aircraft and pay you for the flying hours the machine does with the fleet, giving you some return on your investment. And it does take much of the

Pearson Phillips at the controls

worry out of owning your own aircraft. In general, it can be said that if a business uses an aircraft for about 400 hours a year, it makes sense to own it, and perhaps to pay a commercial pilot too, so that the owner can be relieved of some of his flying when on business.

Of course, there is a great deal of club flying, whether using club aeroplanes, or hiring an aircraft for an event. I was told that the London School of Flying was organising weekend trips to the Channel Isles, Malta, Hamburg, Stornaway and Switzerland. One of these was a ladies-only event, while the men opted to fly to Hamburg—I can't think why! The club briefs the pilots about their routes, etc., and usually provides a technician or an instructor to fly with the party in case there are any snags. These expeditions are very popular with PPL pilots, for they help to give confidence in making long-distance flights abroad. Club Robin International have even organised air rallys to faraway places like Tunisia and West Africa.

Some young people look on learning to fly as the first step in an aviation career. How do you set about breaking into the world of commercial flying? One way, of course, is to enroll full-time at a Flying College, such as the one at Oxford. But this takes a year, and costs some £30,000, so that anyone taking the course needs to be sponsored, which, with the recession in aviation, is not so easy nowadays. Another way in is through military aviation. However, many find their way through from private flying. Starting as I did, by taking the PPL course, they added up their hours after passing the licence until they reached 130, when after a training course, they were able to take an Instructor's examination. Training has to be done at an approved establishment, and takes six to eight weeks. The test is conducted by the Panel of Examiners. If successful, the pilot can become an Assistant Instructor, working under the supervision of the Chief Flying Instructor of a club or school. After six months, the Assistant may then become a fully-fledged instructor. This is the only way

you can be paid for flying at this stage, and the London School of Flying prefers to keep its instructors for at least two years, although having obtained their instrument rating. in some cases, instructors leave quickly, having obtained their instrument rating and commercial licences. But these people are rarely good instructors, I was told. The next stage is perhaps to become a corporate pilot, flying business people—in fact, becoming a sort of aerial chauffeur. Then into the second pilot's seat of a smaller airline—and from there on, luck and airline expansion may bring you to the captain's seat in a big jet, flying for a first-class airline. But in these days, you will need a lot of luck and persistence to make it to there.

So there we are—for the PPL holder, a whole new world of possibilities opens up, whether for fun flying, business or an aviation career. My own flying training was just the first step in a continuing adventure—the adventure of learning to fly. And that, after all, is what this book has been all about.

Index

Bibliography

For technical background reading I found three works of use to me in preparing for the PPL.

1 *Flight Briefing for Pilots* by *N H Birch* and *A E Bramson* (Pitman Publishing), a long-standing four volume manual which has been continuously revised since it first appeared in 1968. I used *Volume 1. An Introductory Manual of Flying Training,* and *Volume 4. Associated Ground Subjects,* covering such things as navigation and meteorology.

2 *Flying Training for the Private Pilot Licence* by *R D Campbell* (Aviation Training Publications Limited, 28a Somerset Street, Northampton, England). It is produced under the auspices of the Aircraft Owners and Pilots Association. Part Two covers the PPL syllabus in great detail.

3 *Private Pilot Studies* by *S E T Taylor* and *H A Parmar* (T & A D Poyser Limited, Berkhamsted). It covers the ground syllabus in racy, chatty fashion (the authors were both ground studies instructors). Particularly good at unravelling the intricacies of air law.

I was also assisted by the **London School of Flying Briefings and Notes** (copyright BLS Aviation Limited) which are issued to students at the beginning of the course, summarising the various lessons.

For other aviation reading matter I recommend a browse through the volumes stocked at many flying schools, or at such specialist bookshops as the one to be found in the Air Touring Shop at Elstree Aerodrome. Fruitful browsing can also be done at the library of the Civil Aviation Authority, Kingsway, London.

Acknowledgements

I would like to acknowledge the help of all at the London School of Flying, Elstree Aerodrome, Hertfordshire, without whom this project would literally not have become airborne. Particular thanks go to Mike McDonnell, the Chief Flying Instructor, and Jeanne McCabe, who taught me. Jeanne's patient and fluent instruction made the writing of the book much easier than it might have been. I have to thank Alan Bramson, doyen of aviation training, for pitching me into this venture in the first place, and both Alan and his colleague Neville Birch for casting their eyes over the text and illustrations. Concerning those illustrations, incidentally, I would like to congratulate those at Playne Design, particularly Art Editor Simon Borrough and his colleagues Nick Hand, Jacquie Govier, Nick Allen, Lois Wigens and Nicholas Rous. for artwork which considerably embellishes the words. Acknowledgement is also due to the Civil Aviation Authority and the Controller of Her Majesty's Stationery Office for permission to reproduce part of the 1980 1:500,000 Aeronautical Chart of Southern England and Wales on pages 125, 128, 129, 130 and 131 (Crown copyright reserved). Finally, my thanks to Ed James of Panshanger Aerodrome, Hertfordshire, who introduced me to the joys of flying a light aircraft and who first taught me to "get the picture right".

Pearson Phillips
July 1982